The Author

Edward O'Relly holds an M.A. in psychology and philosophy and an M.S.P.E. in health, physical education, and recreation from McGill University, Montreal, Canada. He also holds a degree in science from the University of Western Ontario and a degree in physical education from Springfield College, and has done additional postgraduate work at Columbia University. He has written many articles on health, physical education, sports, and sex education, and is currently serving as Editor of Sports Medicine for *Scientific Muscle Training Illustrated.* He was formerly Fitness Consultant and Editorial Director for Vic Tanny Enterprises and Executive Editor for Champion Sports Publications, and has taught health, physical education, and psychology at leading American and Canadian universities.

SEXERCISES
was originally published
by Crown Publishers, Inc.

SEXERCISES

Isometric and Isotonic

Edward O'Relly, M.A., M.S.P.E.

PUBLISHED BY POCKET BOOKS NEW YORK

SEXERCISES

Crown edition published June, 1967

A *Pocket Book* edition
1st printing...........April, 1968

This *Pocket Book* edition includes every word
contained in the original, higher-priced edition. It is printed
from brand-new plates made from completely reset, clear, easy-to-read
type. *Pocket Book* editions are published by Pocket Books, a division
of Simon & Schuster, Inc., 630 Fifth Avenue, New York, N.Y. 10020.
Trademarks registered in the United States and other countries.

L

To my two sons and two daughters
may this book and the progressive sex education
they have received help them to live
healthier, happier, more satisfying lives

CONTENTS

PREFACE

The sex urge is strong, perhaps the strongest of all motivating forces in man. Upon it depended the life of every human now living, and depends the lives of all those yet to be born. Without it, the human race would long ago have ceased to exist.

The sex urge is a normal, natural, fundamental, physiological drive. It is just as much a part of you as the urge to live, and more easily defined.

Lawrence S. Bee, in his *Marriage and Family Relations* (Harper & Row, New York, 1959), says, "Sexual fulfillment is a universally pursued goal. Genital expression of sex has evolved from a form of primordial impregnation to a highly developed form of emotional, intellectual, aesthetic and social experience—a relationship in which the simple biological function is vested with the deepest feelings and intellectual overtones."

Every normal, healthy male and female strives toward the satisfaction of his and her basic physiological and psychological sexual needs. Modern civilization centers around the family unit which is based on marriage. It is good and desirable that men and women seek to get married, to love each other fully and completely as Nature decreed, to have children, to establish a home, and to live healthy, happy, useful, satisfying lives.

Unfortunately, there are forces constantly at work which can undermine the intimate relationships between a man and his wife, turn love into hate, wipe out happiness, destroy marriage, and break up the family unit. Recent statistics show that one out of three marriages ends in divorce or separation, legal or otherwise, and that the number of broken marriages is increasing steadily.

There has also been a tremendous increase in the number of *psychological divorces* where the partners continue to live under the same roof but are separated in all important respects. Frequently, the psychological climate in such homes is more detrimental to all members of the family unit, especially the children, than complete and final separation.

There are a multitude of causes that produce or lead to unhealthy, unhappy, unfulfilled marriages, but not the least of these is sexual maladjustment. The noted psychiatrist, Dr. Frank S. Caprio, in his book *Sex and Love* (Prentice-Hall, Inc.) says: "Beneath our annual harvest of 400,000 divorces, experts agree, almost always lies tragic failure in *sexual love*."

Hundreds of excellent books on sex and marriage have rolled off the press during the past two decades. Innumerable researches have been carried out in various parts of the world covering every aspect of this vital area of human life. Thousands of technical and nontechnical articles have appeared about sex in a multitude of publications. More factual information has been disseminated to the general public about sex in the past generation than in all others put together—and there is room for more. Sex is an integral part of life about which far more is unknown than known.

This book is not a survey of materials already presented elsewhere. It is not a repetition, modification, or condensation of subjects adequately covered by other writers in other books. It does not attempt to raise and answer *all* questions related to sex. It is an entirely *new* book presenting an entirely *new* solution to some of the basic problems of sexual maladjustment. It concentrates on one vital area which has been almost completely overlooked and about which very little authoritative information is available.

This is the neuromuscular and kinesiological aspect of sex with an emphasis on the physiological actions which are basic to the mental, emotional, and psychological factors. This stresses the important effect of the body on the mind (somatopsychic) rather than the effect of the mind on the body (psychosomatic). It makes use of basic tenets advanced by forward-thinking psychologists many years ago as well as modern psychocybernetics. It views the human being as a total goal-seeking entity with mind and body interacting in a dynamic reciprocal relationship.

It is not presented as a cure-all, but rather as one more useful aid to the ailing marriage, and as a preventive of sexual maladjustment for those about to embark upon marriage. It has only one purpose—to help you and your partner enjoy a richer, fuller, more satisfying sex-love life.

It is simple, practical, easy to understand, and easy to follow. It is sensible and logical. It gives you a specific, concrete, step-by-step program of activities that you can follow immediately to make you a better sex-love partner, both mentally and physically.

A wise man once said, "Practice without theory is blind —theory without practice is dead." This book supplies the *plan*—it is up to you to provide the *action*.

EDWARD O'RELLY

CHAPTER 1

YOUR AMAZING
SEX DRIVE

SEXUAL INTERCOURSE

The act of sexual intercourse between man and woman is the natural, logical culmination of the God-given sex drive which permeates every living human being. The sex act was purposely made enjoyable to assure the continuation of the human race. Nature intended us to enjoy sexual intercourse or would have created us otherwise. The wisdom therein was indeed infinite for it has enabled us to survive for countless centuries.

Sexual intercourse is man's only bid for physical immortality. Through it, and only through it, can part of him live on. You are the direct result of a sexual union, so too is every other human now on earth, and all those who preceded them; and so too will be all humans yet to come.

Without the sex drive there would be no sexual intercourse, and without sexual intercourse there would be no human race. Thus, personal survival depends on race survival, because without the race there would be no individuals. Similarly, race survival depends upon the survival of the individuals who make up the human race. Consequently, it is impossible to divorce the will-to-live from the will-to-procreate, for each is dependent on the other, and both rank as the strongest motivating forces in man.

There is nothing wrong about enjoying sexual intercourse, any more than there is anything wrong about enjoying a deep breath of fresh air. Each satisfies a fundamental biological urge, a hunger if you will, that is needed for survival of the race on the one hand and survival of the individual on the other.

Nature works many miracles, but none so remarkable as reproduction and the powerful built-in drive to procreate. No matter how much you study this subject or how much you learn about it, you will never cease to marvel at its intricate, fascinating mysteries.

Your built-in sex drive is linked closely with your very desire to live. It is bound up with everything you do from infancy to old age, and influences all of your thoughts and actions. Your sex glands create internal secretions which affect the functioning of all other glands of internal secretion, including such vitally important endocrine glands as your pancreas, thyroid, parathyroids, adrenal and pituitary glands.

Your sex drive affects your nervous system, your circulatory system, your respiratory system, your digestive system, your excretory system, your muscular system and your endocrine system, as well as your reproductive system. It could not be otherwise, because your sex glands empty their products of internal secretion directly into your bloodstream, which serves every cell, tissue, organ, and system that make up your entire body. It is impossible to divorce your sex drive from your body as a whole because it is an inherent, integral part of it, from birth to death, and influences everything you think or feel or do.

The sex drive is basic to all the sex problems that face man today. Sigmund Freud contended that the restrictions placed upon the human being by society force him to curtail or inhibit his strongest natural desire, that of sex gratification, and that this frustration produces both physiological and psychological tensions that find relief in a host of mental, emotional, and physical outlets. If there were no sex drive it is highly probable that there would be no sex problems as we know them today.

Your sex drive is a natural God-given attribute and just as much a part of your makeup as hunger for food. The organs through which your sex drive expresses itself are just as important to you as your heart, lungs, kidneys, or liver. Sex organs and sex functions are just as common, just as normal, and just as essential as any other organs or functions. You can no more deny the desire for sexual gratification than you can deny the desire for food when hungry.

No problem has ever been solved by ignoring it or running away from it, and the problems of sex are no exception. We must view sex intelligently and objectively, facing facts honestly and squarely, and adjusting ourselves accordingly.

The sex drive, like all other drives associated with the satisfaction of basic organic needs, has a definite unlearned core. It can be found in all humans, whether primitive or civilized, educated or uneducated, and regardless of race, color, or habitat. Physiologically there is a change in the chemical composition of the blood, which is brought about by the injection of a sex hormone into the bloodstream. The presence of this hormone in large amounts upsets the chemical equilibrium of the blood and sets up internal tensions that seek release through sexual intercourse.

In animals, the secretion of the sex hormone, the cycles of sex activity, and even sex behavior itself, are totally unlearned. In humans, though the secretion is unlearned and there is measurable periodicity in females, the resultant sex behavior is greatly modified by past learning and experience. In addition, because of their higher mental and emotional organization, there are psychological involvements which are unknown in the animal world.

In primitive societies, when young people reached sexual maturity, they were considered ready for mating and found natural outlets for their sex urges. There were no frustrations, reservations, or inhibitions, and the sexual act could be enjoyed fully and freely to the utmost capacity of

the two participants. Sexual intercourse was a simple, uncomplicated response to a fundamental biological urge.

Modern civilization has become more and more complex,
and a great deal more time is required to prepare youth to
assume the responsibilities of adulthood. As a result, mating is now delayed long beyond the peak period of the
sexual drive in the male, and usually well after sexual maturity has been reached by the female. Our society demands
that the sexual urge be controlled until after marriage but
does not really practice what it preaches. Consequently,
sexual expression becomes a clandestine matter with overtones of guilt.

To complicate matters still more, there is still considerable puritanical carry-over from the strict, straitlaced eras
we have left behind; there is conflict in the mores of three
generations all living at the same time; there is a definite
lag between what people profess and their actions; and
finally, there is the deliberate exploitation of the sex urge
to sell products and services of every kind. What was once
a relatively simple, basic, physiological drive has become
so diffused, so colored, so modified, twisted, frustrated, or
sublimated that it is almost impossible to recognize the
endless ramifications.

Unfortunately, this has led to fears, doubts, misgivings,
guilt feelings, unhealthy attitudes, internal conflicts, repres-
sions, tensions, psychological complexes, sexual deviations,
impatience, frigidity, and numerous other sexual problems.

SIMPLIFICATION IS NEEDED

If ever a "back to Nature" trend was in order, it is in
the realm of sex. A healthy, wholesome, uncomplicated attitude toward the sex organs and their functions is definitely
needed. Sex organs are constructed of the same basic materials as all other organs of the body. Sex glands are
similar in all major respects to all other endocrine glands
in the body. Sex functions, when viewed objectively, differ
little from the functions of other organs of the body.

Originally you were one single fertilized cell, which di-
vided and grew and multiplied until you became billions

of cells, organized into various tissues to form different organs to make up and serve your body as a whole. Your sex organs are no more mysterious than your heart or lungs. Each has a vital job to perform. The difference between your sexual organs and any other organ in your body is mainly one of cell differentiation. Similarly, if you view the act of sexual intercourse in a purely objective manner, it is just another physiological function, no more right or wrong than respiration or defecation. Attitudes toward sexual organs and sexual functions are entirely learned, varying from age to age, culture to culture, from one community to the next, from person to person, and even within the individual himself.

The sex drive is fixed. It can be misdirected, distorted, thwarted, or sublimated, but it cannot be eradicated. Fortunately, attitudes can be changed, and the full power of the sex drive can be utilized as Nature intended, to bring to you and your sex partner the highest possible peak of sheer physical joy.

Psychiatrists are changing sex attitudes every day, but the process is long and costly. Essentially the changes are made only by the patient, not by his analyst—the latter acts more as a sounding board and a guide, helping the patient to see himself as he really is. The approach is psychological—mind affecting body—in the broader sense of the term, "psychosomatic."

Our approach in this book is exactly opposite: it is physical—body affecting mind—in the broader sense of the term, "somatopsychic."

THE SOMATOPSYCHIC APPROACH

In 1880, the great American psychologist, William James, said, "we do not tremble because we are afraid, we are afraid because we tremble." A similar but entirely independent theory was proposed about the same time by the noted Danish psychologist, C. G. Lange. Their work in this field, which became known as the James-Lange Theory, expressed the belief that emotional or "psychic" states have a bodily or "somatic" origin. Years were to pass before the opposite term was to become popular, namely "psychosomatic," which expresses the fact that certain "somatic" or bodily conditions have a "psychological" origin. It is only within the past decade that the term "psychosomatic" has become part of the vocabulary of the informed layman, and not much before this that "psychosomatic medicine" was recognized by most physicians.

Still more recently it has been rediscovered that bodily actions or states also have an effect upon mental or emotional states, and the term "somatopsychic" is beginning to appear more frequently.

Benjamin Disraeli, in *Vivian Grey* (1826), wrote, "Experience is the child of Thought, and Thought is the child of Action." Centuries earlier, there was written into the Proverbs of the Old Testament, "As he thinketh in his heart, so is he."

Mind and body are an inseparable unity. Neither can exist without the other. Thoughts take place in a physical medium. Every thought results in some physical change, and every physical action has its mental counterpart. The distinctions between mind and body are largely academic.

Sexual intercourse is a physical act, performed by physical beings, utilizing physical organs, powered by physical muscles. The psychic involvements—mental, emotional, psychological—are fully recognized, but in this book we are directing our attention to the *physical* aspects because we can actually feel and see them and exert direct control over them. We know that body affects mind, and by training the body to perform effectively and efficiently, we must beneficially modify the mental, emotional, and psychological aspects of the sexual act.

Hundreds of books have been written by psychiatrists, psychologists, and sexologists that "treat of the mind"—that seek to solve the sex problems of man through the psychological approach. This is the first that "treats of the body"—that seeks to solve problems through the physical approach.

CHAPTER 2

WE HAVE BECOME A RACE OF SEX CRIPPLES

THE PHYSICAL DETERIORATION OF MAN

Automation and mechanization are robbing us of our health, strength, stamina, flexibility, vigor, agility, and neuromuscular coordination. Never in the entire history of mankind has there been such a great need for physical fitness, and with the development of each new labor-saving device, this need becomes increasingly greater.

Machines are replacing human muscles. Planes, trains, automobiles, and escalators are making legs almost useless. We are rapidly degenerating into a race of button-pushers. Most of our waking hours are spent on our posteriors— sitting, driving, watching, riding, and otherwise engaged in sedentary pursuits. What with TV and spectator sports, even recreation is becoming predominantly passive.

Modern science and technology have brought us the highest standards of living the world has ever seen. We can justifiably be proud of our fantastic progress and unparalleled material possessions. Yet these self-same technical achievements, which are bringing us so many of the good things of life, also contain the seeds of our destruction.

We are *living* human beings, made up of countless billions of *living* cells which are organized into a multitude of *living* tissues, organs, and systems. We are acting creatures as well as thinking creatures. We possess muscles as well as brains. We are mobile, moving, manipulating beings. Our muscles have enabled us to make the machines which are replacing muscles.

This is the age of the intellect. Yet minds are useless without muscles. At this very moment studies are being made which indicate that the porpoise, with its relatively bigger brain, may have a superior intelligence to man's. Even if this were the case, the porpoise will never equal man in scientific achievement because his body, lacking feet and hands, does not permit him to translate thinking into action. Man is superior to other creatures not only brainwise but musclewise, but as his muscles deteriorate, so too does his overall superiority.

Stop to think for a moment what you would be capable of doing with the same brain you now possess if it was housed in the body of a snake. With no means of communication and no muscle-powered, brain-directed hands and feet, you would be as helpless and unproductive as the snake, despite your vastly superior brain.

Physical exercise is absolutely essential to keep your living machinery in the best possible working order. Muscles increase in efficiency with use, and deteriorate with disuse. Lack of physical activity leads to muscular atrophy. Atrophy manifests itself by a wasting away of the muscle tissues, by loss of muscle tone, and by increasing flabbiness. Unused muscles show a progressive loss of strength, stamina, flexibility, endurance, speed, and neuromuscular coordination.

You need regular, systematic physical exercise to keep every muscle in your body strong, healthy, flexible, and efficient. You need regular planned exercise to keep all your vital internal organs healthy and functioning efficiently. In fact, every cell, tissue, organ, and system in your entire body can be beneficially affected by regular, systematic exercise. However, in this book we are primarily interested in specific exercises that will improve those muscles which are directly involved in performing the sex act.

SEXUAL INTERCOURSE IS A PHYSICAL ACT

No amount of moralizing, emotionalizing, or rationalizing can alter the fact that sexual intercourse is a physical act which involves coordinated muscular activity on the part of the persons involved. True, there are mental and emotional involvements, but the union itself is *physical,* and all the actions that take place are definitely *muscular.* Without muscles there can be no movement, and without movements there can be no act of sexual intercourse.

Practically all the muscles involved in the sex act are also involved in other physical activities. Consequently, their deterioration from diminishing use as a result of automation has a definite negative effect on their use in the performance of the sex act.

MODERN LIVING CREATES SEXUAL CRIPPLES

Unused muscles diminish in strength, stamina, vigor, endurance, elasticity, tonus, agility, flexibility, speed of reaction, power and neuromuscular coordination. Physical fitness tests, given to thousands of persons over a period of many years, prove conclusively that sedentary living produces a steady loss of motor capacity and a gradual deterioration in all other muscular attributes. The current world-wide concern about the fitness of our youth is a reflection of these findings. One study, carried out in a wealthy urban community, found grandmothers to be more physically fit than their teenage granddaughters.

Modern civilization is gradually reducing our efficiency as sexual partners by making us less physically capable of performing the sex act.

More and more, both men and women are complaining of back troubles. Faulty posture heads the list of causes. Good posture requires strong, efficient, well-coordinated muscles, especially in the lower back. Unused muscles, tendons, and ligaments tend to become shortened and lose their elasticity, resulting in sustained postural imbalance and many unnecessary aches and pains. Muscular weakness and muscular tightness are responsible for more back troubles than all the other causes put together.

No man or woman can be a good sex partner with a "trick back," with a back so weakened from sedentary sitting and generally lack of exercise that he or she may suffer painful muscle spasms in the middle of the sex act. It is also difficult to perform the sex act satisfactorily with a back that lacks muscular strength, flexibility, and staying power.

Another modern trend which has reduced the efficiency of countless thousands of sex partners is obesity. Eating more and exercising less has added considerably to the average weight of both men and women. Unfortunately, this extra weight gathers first in the abdominal region contributing to postural disorders, lack of flexibility in the midregion, flabby abdominal muscles, a sagging stomach, and weak back muscles. The extra weight at the front pulls you forward so that you must lean backward to maintain your balance. Thus your back muscles are under constant tension, and tend to shorten, thereby reducing your normal range of action, and producing painful muscle spasms when subjected to even the slightest extra exertion.

Exercise can help to prevent and cure these undesirable sex-crippling conditions.

FLABBY BODIES DETRACT FROM SEX ENJOYMENT

In spite of man's muscular deterioration, or perhaps because of it, we admire well-built, trim, firm, youthful, attractive bodies more than ever before. This could be a subconscious reaching for something we know we are losing. It might also account for the tremendous increase of interest in spectator sports. Through vicarious identification with well-built, athletic performers we "satisfy," or appease, the inner gnawing of an ancient survival instinct. The Romans before us did this, at their peak of greatness, when they substituted slaves for muscles, and were destroyed from within by the slow corrosion of luxury.

No man is sexually attracted to a woman who has a flabby, disproportionate figure. The "other" woman never looks like that. Nor is she the skinny, stoop-shouldered type. Few men marry such women, but, unfortunately, too many wives eventually become physically unattractive because of lack of exercise.

Of course, the same holds true the other way around. In fact, more men let themselves go after marriage than women—eating too much, drinking too much, smoking too much, and exercising too little. Invariably the "other" man is physically more attractive and possesses a more youthful, masculine body.

No husband or wife, no matter how much in love, how completely satisfied with each other, or how faithful, is blind to the charms of others of the opposite sex. There would be no Rock Hudsons or Jayne Mansfields if we did not react to sex-love symbols. We are subconsciously attracted to those of the opposite sex who fit our sex-love images, who look sexually desirable.

These sex-love images have been created for us by the books we read, by newspapers, radio, TV, movies, and every other medium of communication. Mostly, they have been created by advertising men anxious to sell a service or product by linking it with the powerful sex hunger.

Every man and woman strives to fit this image in order to be sexually attractive to members of the opposite sex. We do this with the clothes we wear, the toothpastes and deodorants we use, the cars we drive, the social activities we learn, and with our overall physical appearance. To a large extent we cannot do otherwise, because trends, styles, and images are created for us, and various social and psychological pressures are developed to keep us in line.

Thus, each of us is forced to compete with the "ideal" sex image our mate possesses. True, we can close our eyes, or turn out the lights during intimate relationships, but we cannot blot out the mental or tactile picture of an undesirable body.

Regular, systematic exercise can help each of us to obtain and maintain a well-proportioned, energetic, and sexually attractive body.

HAVE A HEART FOR SEX

There has been a tremendous increase in cardiovascular ailments in recent years. One of the world's leading heart specialists, Dr. Paul Dudley White, blames much of this on automation, soft living, overeating and underexercising. He tells us in *The New York Times Magazine* (June 23, 1957) that exercise has an immediate beneficial effect upon the circulation, that it can help to prevent blood clots, that it is essential for keeping the heart in good condition, and that it is as vital to good health as food and sleep.

Dr. Thomas Cureton, director of the University of Illinois Physical Fitness Laboratory, recently said, "The most effective way to fight the staggering toll of degenerative diseases is through regular, vigorous, sustained, sweat-producing physical exertion."

A strong healthy heart and an efficiently working circulatory system are as important to the act of sexual intercourse as they are to an Olympic athlete running the 100-meter sprint, and every bit as taxing. This was most dramatically shown by tests carried out at the National Institutes of Health to determine the physiological costs of the sex act. Married couples, tested by scientific instruments, showed an increase of heartbeats from as low as 70 per minute to as high as 192 per minute in less than sixty seconds, with a tripling in breathing rate. This is comparable to the most vigorous athletic endeavor.

No coach would permit an untrained athlete to give forth with such an explosive burst of physical effort, yet millions of untrained sex partners do this again and again with no concern for their gradually increasing exhaustion. Specialized physical training for the satisfactory and safe performance of the sex act is definitely indicated.

STRENGTH AND STAMINA ARE PREREQUISITES

Sexual intercourse is a physical act requiring both strength and stamina for its satisfactory performance.

Neither of these attributes develops of itself, and both are diminishing with the decline of physical man.

It takes a certain amount of physical strength to support oneself, and still more strength to support the weight of another, in the various sex positions. Muscular strength is also required to produce action, and the more vigorous this is, the more strength it takes.

If one or both partners are muscularly weak, especially in those muscles directly involved in the sex act, then the performance thereof will be greatly limited, and the satisfaction derived therefrom greatly reduced.

Sexual intercourse also requires sustained muscular action, both static and dynamic, and this demands the development of stamina and endurance. Where one or both partners lack the staying power to complete the sex act, this can result only in frustration and disappointment. If the act is difficult to complete, or exhausting, it cannot bring the enjoyment it should, and paves the way for future difficulties or failures.

Both strength and stamina can be developed through regular systematic exercise. Strength comes from exercising against progressively increasing work loads. Stamina comes from gradually increasing the duration of exercise bouts.

NEUROMUSCULAR SKILL IS ESSENTIAL

To learn even the simplest coordinated activity requires correct practice. It takes months of persistent effort to learn to walk. Even when fully mature, it takes years to learn how to hit a golf ball skillfully.

Sexual intercourse is a far more complicated act, with its many variations, moods, positions, and actions; and it involves two persons who must synchronize their movements to achieve the ultimate in mutual stimulation and satisfaction.

All this cannot be learned by instinct or intuition. Nor can it be learned by incorrect practice, or even correct practice, without much effort, if the basic equipment is deficient.

The right kind of exercise can increase the range of movement at all of your important joints by increasing the flexibility of your muscles, tendons, and ligaments. Such exercise can bring unused muscles into play, thereby increasing your agility and dexterity. It can exercise important muscles in different ways, enabling you to exert more control over the movement of various body parts. It can increase your capacity for performing all kinds of skillful activities, including those involved in the very important sex act.

Trained muscles work more effectively and efficiently with less mental or physical effort. The higher the degree of neuromuscular coordination, the lower are the physiological costs. Finally, the more skillful your sex muscles become, the greater will be your contribution to the sex act, and the more pleasure and satisfaction will both you and your partner derive therefrom.

There is a tremendous need for a comprehensive, scientific exercise program aimed specifically at rehabilitating all those muscles which are essential to the successful performance of the sex act. This book supplies such a program.

SCIENTIFIC REHABILITATION

Ironically, we know more about anatomy, physiology, and kinesiology—more about the makeup and functioning of man—than ever before. In an age of mass deterioration we are living longer than ever before and are producing the best athletes the world has ever seen.

We know more about scientific muscle training today than at any other time in the entire history of mankind, but very little of this knowledge is utilized by the average person to improve his strength, flexibility, endurance, or neuromuscular coordination.

The various exercises prescribed in this book are designed to prevent muscular deterioration where none now exists and to rehabilitate those muscles which have been allowed to deteriorate.

All the exercises should be performed isotonically and isometrically unless otherwise specifically indicated. First should come the isotonic contractions, since these involve movement, and the sex act is largely one of action. Then should come the isometric (static) contractions to aid in the maintenance of muscle strength and tone.

For the isotonic exercises, you force the part involved through the greatest possible range of motion, going from one extreme to the other, and always trying to increase the range of action.

For the isometric exercises you simply "hold" the contraction for the counts (approximately six seconds). It is necessary to do each isometric exercise only once per day for strength building, and just once every two weeks for maintaining the strength which has been developed.

Any isotonic (movement) exercise described below can easily be converted into an isometric (no movement) exercise by simply *holding* each extreme of the movement for ten counts (approximately six seconds).

For example, in the exercise "Erect, Standing with Back Against Wall" (page 71), you are instructed to thrust your pelvis forward and upward as far as it will go and then downward and backward as far as it will go. You go directly from one extreme to the other, always striving to increase the range of motion. This is an isotonic exercise because it involves muscular contraction with *movement*.

To convert this into an isometric exercise (with no movement) you would force your pelvis forward and upward as far as it will go and *hold* this position until you count to ten (approximately six seconds). Then you would force your pelvis downward and backward as far as it will go and *hold* this position until you count to ten (approximately six seconds). In other words, you go from one extreme of the exercise to the other, and hold each of the opposite extremes for ten counts (approximately six seconds).

Exactly the same procedure is followed to convert any other isotonic (movement) exercise into an isometric (no movement) exercise.

CHAPTER 3

WHERE SEXUAL
RELATIONSHIPS
GO WRONG

HUSBANDS AND WIVES WHO DISAPPOINT

Too many husbands and wives are disappointed in each other as sexual partners. Each feels cheated by the other, though they may never admit it, even to themselves. The ultimate realization is rarely as great as the expectation. Though they may be reasonably happy with each other, this invariably leads to doubts about their own contribution to the sex act or that of their partner. It could lead to speculation, to impotence or frigidity, and to outright infidelity.

Before marriage women do everything in their power to look and act desirable—to promise sexual satisfaction. They do this with their clothes, their makeup, their perfumes, their facial expressions, by emphasizing sex-appealing parts of their anatomy, by the way they sit and walk, and by otherwise exploiting sex symbols and fitting themselves to current sex images. Some of this is deliberate but much of it is subconscious.

For the most part the current sex images are created by men, aided and abetted by women, who are purposely utilizing the powerful sex drive to sell a product or service. Their female images promise sexual satisfaction through radio, TV, movies, newspapers, magazines, billboards, and all other media. The die is cast, and every female is judged by the degree of approximation to the "ideal" pattern. The greater the built-in "sex promise" the more sought-after is the female, and the greater the disappointment to the male who wins her.

Millions of dollars are spent annually creating *desirable* female sex images, and millions more are spent by the fairer sex striving to fill these images and make herself sexually attractive to men, but little is spent on *teaching or learning* how to fulfill the sex promises.

Vance Packard in his penetrating book on motivational research tells how extensively the sex urge is being exploited to "channel our unthinking habits, our purchasing decisions, and our thought processes." He says, "The use of mass psychoanalysis to guide campaigns of persuasion has become the basis of a multimillion-dollar industry. Professional persuaders have seized upon it . . . for more effective ways to sell us their wares—whether products, ideas, attitudes, candidates, goals or states of mind. The sale to us of billions of dollars' worth of . . . products is being significantly affected, if not revolutionized, by this approach. . . ." (Vance Packard, *The Hidden Persuaders,* Pocket Books, Inc., New York, 1960)

Male sex images as well as female are also deliberately created and publicized, but the impact is different because man is the seeker. However, women are taking a more prominent and dominant part in our society, and the male needs reassurance of his masculinity. The advertising expert gives it to him in the cigars he smokes, the cars he drives, the clothes he wears, the after-shaving lotion he uses, and a multitude of other ways. Thus, males, like females, are promising something they cannot deliver—sexual fulfillment.

By fitting himself to the current male sex symbols, modern man, before marriage, gives the impression that he is a strong, masculine man capable of taking the lead in the sex act to the full satisfaction of the feminine female. Through vicarious identification he fancies himself "a great lover," "a man-about-town," and, to add to the ultimate disillusionment, conveys the same misconception to his future sex partner. The *moment of truth* which attends the merging of two sex images can be most shattering to the female dream world and the inflated male ego.

Failure to satisfy can have far-reaching negative psychological effects, undermining partners' confidence in each other and themselves. What should have been the ultimate expression of sex-satisfying love becomes instead a passive duty for the wife and a disappointment for the husband. This could lead to loss of mutual respect, to sexual incompatibility, to a search for sex satisfaction elsewhere, to psychological divorce, or full legal divorce. It could also lead to frigidity on the part of the wife or impotence in the husband, or both.

Dr. Frank S. Caprio, speaking from his lengthy experience as a psychiatrist, says: "When a couple tell me they wish to dissolve the marriage because of money quarrels, in-law interference, or some personality-clash, I assume that the *love-relationship* was a poor one to begin with. I also discover that in almost every case there is evidence of sexual disharmony. What can you expect when there is an absence of love and sexual satisfaction?" (*Sex and Love*)

A survey of the professional literature on marital difficulties points most emphatically to sexual dissatisfaction as the most important, single, basic, causative factor.

HUSBANDS BLAME THEIR WIVES

Most men are dissatisfied by the lack of responsiveness on the part of their wives. Psychiatrists, marriage counsellors, social workers, and others concerned with marital problems report that men complain more about this than anything else. Dr. Olivier Loras says, "The husband complains about his wife's lack of enthusiasm, her passivity or her indifference to the marital act . . . she remains 'cold'; she does not participate in the climax. This often leads him to seek the company of other women, which in turn aggravates his marital situation." (*Frigidity and Marital Con-*

flict, Sex Education Library, Health Publications, New York, 1960)

Nothing hurts a man's ego more than the gnawing belief that he is a dismal failure as a sex partner. How can he be a "man" if he cannot function as a man? He must *know* that he is a success as a sex mate. If he cannot arouse and fully satisfy his wife there must be something wrong with him—*or his wife.* How much easier on his ego if he can blame his wife.

If the wife is unattractive or physically unfit, if she is always too tired, if she is constantly complaining about ill health, if she is weak or lacks skill, if she offers lame excuses, or if she does not participate fully for any other reason, the blame will be more easily laid on her. To reassure himself of his own sex prowess the disappointed husband may look elsewhere for sexual satisfaction. If the "other" woman is experienced, invites instead of rejects his advances, is an active rather than a passive partner, and enjoys a full orgasm, his faith in himself will be restored.

It is a well-known fact that many men who are actually impotent with their wives are not impotent with other women, especially when the latter are skilled and make the men feel that they are capable sex partners. A husband needs approval, and this comes from knowing that he is capable of arousing and fully satisfying his wife.

Differences in sex desires between husbands and wives are another source of friction and frustration. "One of the most frequently cited complaints is that of differences in sex appetite, with men desiring coitus more frequently than their wives." (Clifford Kirkpatrick, *The Family,* The Ronald Press Company, New York, 1955)

Lack of desire, of responsiveness, of participation, passive acceptance, or outright rejection on the part of the wife is invariably linked with the absence of pleasure in the sex act and hence lack of orgasm. It is inconceivable that any wife could remain passive or "cold" while experiencing peak sexual stimulation and final sexual fulfillment.

Drs. Kroger and Freed state that "Gynecologists and psychiatrists especially are aware that perhaps 75 percent of all women derive little or no pleasure from the sexual act. Many women not only experience no pleasure, but actually suffer pain and revulsion." ("Psychosomatic Aspects of Sterility," *American Journal of Obstetrics and Gynecology,* 1950)

There is universal agreement in professional circles that the causes of frigidity and associated complaints are primarily "psychic" rather than "somatic," mental and emotional rather than physical, in a word, "psychosexual." Such things are explained as resulting from inadequate or faulty sex information, puritanical attitudes, guilt feelings, anxiety, fear, conflicts, feelings of sexual inadequacy, inhibition, frustration, lack of self-confidence, ego-deflation, emotional "blocks," prudery, restrictive religious upbringing, sexual incompatibility of parents, hush-hush attitudes toward sex, confusion as to respective sex roles, deliberate coloring of the sex act as something that is wrong or evil, and lack of knowledge about the makeup and functions of her own sex organs or those of her husband. The emphasis has been on the mind affecting the body. Frigidity is believed to be primarily psychosomatic.

LITTLE IS SAID ABOUT LACK OF PHYSICAL ABILITY

Psychiatrists, psychologists, sexologists, and others concerned with the problems of sex inadequacy are freeing women from the psychic causes of frigidity and associated complaints, but civilization is producing more and more women who are physically incapable of performing the sex act. No one teaches our women *how* to perform the sexual act. Before marriage they are taught how to sew and cook and take care of a house, but seldom are they taught how to take care of a husband. Countless hours are spent learning a multitude of physical skills ranging from playing a piano to water skiing, but not one minute is spent acquiring skill in an area upon which hinges her entire future happiness and usually that of her husband and children as well.

No one expects to become an expert at anything without training—except sexual intercourse. No one in his right mind who has never skied would attempt a ski jump on his very first try. We practice even the simplest of physical activities in order to develop neuromuscular skill.

Dr. Frederick R. Steggerda says, "*I am fit to do things you cannot do because of the type of physical activities I have forced my nervous system to adjust itself to.*" (*The Role of the Nervous System in Fitness,* Exercise and Fitness [Collection of Papers on Exercise and Fitness] 1960)

No one is an expert at anything automatically or instinctively. The more complicated the neuromuscular coordination, the more training is required to master the activity. Thus, walking a slack wire takes more practice than walking on the ground.

Dr. Elbert Tokay says, "The untrained subject will stumble, both mentally and physically, more often than the trained. . . . Consistent exercise, aside from making us feel better, can help our bodies to become more adequate for the demands placed upon them." (*Fundamentals of Physiology,* Barnes & Noble, Inc., New York, 1959)

From a neuromuscular standpoint, most wives are grossly inept as sexual partners. They not only lack skill but are also deficient in strength, stamina, flexibility, tonus, condition, and associated attributes in all muscles involved in the sexual act. In a word, they are completely *untrained* for the efficient performance of their part in the important act of sexual intercourse. Consequently, they not only fail to satisfy their husbands, but also fail to satisfy themselves.

The special exercise program outlined in this book was devised for the express purpose of remedying this negative "sex-crippling" condition. Each *sexercise* is aimed at training the wife's sex muscles to function with maximum skill and efficiency to bring both her and her husband the utmost in pleasurable sex satisfaction. With skill come self-confidence and a radical change in one's self-image. With enjoyable fulfillment comes the desire for repetition. Active practice for the sex act leads logically to active participation. It is difficult, or even impossible, to train systematically to improve one's skill as a sex partner without reducing or eliminating the concomitant psychological inhibitions. *Doing* can influence thinking, just as thinking influences doing. Skillful doing eradicates feelings of inferiority and inadequacy, fear of failure, apathy, and both mental and physical stumbling.

The sex training program described here will give the wife *control* over her sex muscles, enabling her to determine the range, direction, speed, duration, vigor, and intensity of her sex movements. The sexercises will *educate* her sex muscles and condition them for efficient, active, skillful participation in the sex act. They will help to reduce or eliminate some of the basic physical and psychical causes of sexual incompatibility.

WIVES BLAME THEIR HUSBANDS

It is doubtful if any sex book has ever been written which does not directly or indirectly place the responsibility for leadership and direction in the sex act upon the husband's shoulders. Not only is he expected to educate his wife in sex matters, but upon him falls most of the blame if she fails to perform adequately and does not achieve sexual satisfaction. Most sex books are filled with do's and don'ts for the husband. He is exhorted to be kind, gentle, firm, positive, patient, considerate, and loving. He is told to use endearing words, to be sure to indulge in lengthy precoital stimulation and postcoital attention. He must adjust himself to his wife's varying moods, needs, and desires. His wife must come first in every sense of the word. It is his duty to make sure that she experiences ecstatic orgasm with each sexual union.

Dissatisfied wives invariably blame their husbands. Were not they promised sexual fulfillment before marriage? Do not the books stress the husband's responsibility for the wife's complete sexual satisfaction? Rarely does a frigid woman say, "Doctor! I'm a poor sex partner"—"My faulty attitude toward sex is to blame"—"I am pathetically ignorant about sex." More often the husband is "selfish," "thinks only of sex," "forces himself upon her," "satisfies himself," "rushes through the act," "turns over and goes to sleep," "is clumsy," "doesn't try to satisfy her," "is an animal," and so on.

It is true that there are some husbands who are guilty of some of these things some of the time, but the blame far outweighs the guilt. However, we are interested not so much in the husband's responsibilities, but in those remediable conditions about which nothing has been written. Modern man, like modern woman, is deteriorating physically. Increased flabbiness and decreased flexibility are making him less capable of functioning efficiently. Diminishing strength, stamina, vigor, endurance, power, agility, and all-around physical fitness are making him less effective as a sex partner. Automation and mechanization are producing more and more men who are seriously handicapped in the performance of the sex act.

Even before this onslaught of progressive physical degeneration, few men, if any, were skilled at sexual intercourse in the same sense that they are skilled at golf, tennis, or casting. No man expects to become good at any sport without a great deal of training. Yet all men seem to believe that they can master the complicated, coordinated physical skill involved in sexual intercourse without instruction, conditioning, training, or practice.

In our sexually backward civilization, no one ever teaches our men or women how to perform the vitally important act of sexual intercourse. Woodworking and cooking rate special instructors, but learning one of the most far-reaching, life-molding functions known to man is left to blind, stumbling chance. From a neuromuscular standpoint, modern husbands are not much better than modern wives as sex partners, and both are getting progressively worse.

The *sexercises* outlined in this book were designed to benefit both husbands and wives in an area of gross neglect. They are especially valuable to the husband, who usually takes the more dominant and more active role. They are aimed at giving him more control over his sex muscles so that he can perform the sex act more effectively and efficiently, thereby bringing more joy and satisfaction to his wife and himself.

The practice of these special exercises will reach all muscles involved in the sex act, improving their tonus, condition, and functional ability. This sex *training* program will help make the husband a skillful performer, physically speaking, and should remove his doubts or feelings of inadequacy in that respect. The resulting increased self-confidence should in turn help to remove some of the psychological causes of his inefficiency as a sex partner, and help to overcome impotence.

BOTH BLAME SEX DIFFERENCES

For generations much of the blame for disappointing marital relationships has been placed on differences in sexual response. Male sex organs are largely outside of the body. Female sex organs are largely inside of the body. Males are the pursuers, females the pursued. Men are aroused easily and quickly. Women are aroused slowly and with much difficulty. Practically all men reach orgasm the first time they have intercourse. Many women take weeks or months to reach an orgasm, and some never do.

Obviously there must be fixed, basic differences in sex response, or so it was believed, despite the fact that there were many exceptions. Women *knew* that they were more passive than men, that it took them longer to be aroused, and that a climax was harder for them to achieve. Books on sex tell husbands how to adjust their lovemaking to these "inalterable" sex differences. Since the responsibility for success fell upon the husband so too did the blame for failure.

What about the exceptions? What about those women whose sexual responsiveness equalled that of their husbands, whose speed of arousal was as great, and final orgasmic climax as frequent and intense? What about those women whose sexual desire and capacity equalled or surpassed that of men?

Recent research indicates that men and women are not so far apart in their degree of sexual capacity, responsiveness, speed of arousal, and ultimate orgasm as previously believed, providing their sexual skills are fully developed.

Dr. Lawrence S. Bee says, ". . . men and women are not as different in their sexual responsiveness or the speed of their arousal, as has commonly been believed. Now, and note the qualification carefully, *when a man and a woman have developed their full sexual capacities,* the length of time it takes to be aroused and to achieve orgasm is about the same in women as in men, that is, women are not necessarily slower to respond or less ardent. There is some evidence that they may respond more deeply, since many women experience several orgasms during a single coital engagement and about three percent actually swoon, momentarily losing consciousness."

The sex training program presented in this book is aimed at developing the sexual capabilities of both husbands and wives to the fullest possible degree to reduce or eliminate differences in responsiveness, speed of arousal, and orgasm.

WIVES CAN HELP THEMSELVES ACHIEVE ORGASM

It is so easy to place the blame for sex failure on our partners that we fail to see where we ourselves have failed. In any joint effort, responsibility for success or failure must be jointly shared. This is especially true in intimate man-wife relationships. Nevertheless, there are also individual responsibilities in the sex act, not only to your partner, but to yourself. Each partner must not only strive to satisfy the other but must also strive to satisfy himself or herself.

Women are especially guilty of *un*selfishness. Most are more anxious to satisfy their husbands than themselves. The majority tend to cloak their lack of sex desire, responsiveness, and orgasm. Many who feel pain or revulsion will endure the act without open complaint. However, it is highly unlikely that the husband is really deceived. Subconsciously he will know that he has failed, and his wife's pretense of martyrdom could easily destroy his faith in himself as a sex partner and lead to impotence.

It would perhaps be better if the unsatisfied wife demanded sexual satisfaction, for then the matter would be brought out in the open, and positive steps could be taken to remedy the unhappy situation. Certainly the wife should do everything in her power to achieve complete sexual fulfillment, not only for her own pleasure and her own mental and physical health, but also for her husband's.

There are ways, apart from those already mentioned, whereby the wife can directly assure herself of maximum sex stimulation regardless of the skill of her sex partner. The three most important and most neglected are as follows:

(1) *Labial Pressures*—The folds of skin on either side of the opening of the vagina are known as lips or labia. They form part of a highly sensitive erogenous zone. During intercourse, the pressures against this entire area can be increased or decreased at will by tensing and relaxing the gluteus muscles and by thrusting the pelvic area forward and backward. Except in extreme cases of overweight, the male pubic region is firm and hard because of the bony pelvis immediately beneath the flesh adjacent to the male penis. Therefore, the female can, through her own pelvic manipulations, exert as much pressure upon her labia as she desires.

Of course, this requires trained muscles, with the necessary degree of strength, stamina, flexibility, and neuromuscular control to perform the right movements effectively and efficiently. The *sexercise* program presented in this book was specifically designed to meet these very important requirements.

(2) *Clitoric Stimulation*—The clitoris is a small erectile organ in the female which corresponds to the penis in the male. It is situated above the vaginal opening where the labia minora come together. The distance from the vaginal opening varies from a half inch to a little more than an inch. The clitoris is well supplied with nerves and blood vessels and, like the male penis, is capable of erection under sexual stimulation.

The clitoris has long been known as the seat of sexual stimulation because orgasm can be reached through the manipulation of this organ alone. Dr. Aurelle says, "The clitoris is a major seat of sex sensation in a woman. Stimulation of this organ, during or apart from intromission, usually leads to climax. It is the most sensitive sex organ in the female body." (S. H. Aurelle, M.D., *Structure and Function of the Sex Organs,* Sex Education Library, Health Publications, New York, 1960)

By thrusting her pelvis forward and tilting it downward,

the trained wife can expose her clitoris to maximum stimulation during the sex act. With flexibility and control in the muscles involved, she can coordinate her movements with those of her husband, no matter how unskilled he may be, thereby obtaining greatest possible clitoric stimulation and, in most cases, the fullest possible clitoric orgasm.

The *sexercise* program that follows will give the wife this vitally important pelvic control if conscientiously followed, enabling her to move her pelvic region up, down, in, out, forward, backward, sideward, and in a circular motion. It will permit her to participate actively in her own sexual satisfaction, and give her control over certain conditions which can lead directly to her own orgasm. The tremendous value of clitoric control, to both herself and her husband, in terms of complete sex fulfillment cannot be overemphasized.

To begin with, it is difficult or impossible to hold back mentally and emotionally if you let go physically. Thus the active training for, and the active participation in, the sex act has a powerful psychological effect, helping the wife to overcome any inhibitions she may have. In addition, the thrilling rewards she receives through her skillful participation stimulate her sexual desire and encourages repetition of the sex act. Finally, there will be far less tendency for the wife to blame the husband for sex failures over which she herself exercises so much control.

The wife's full participation and satisfaction will greatly enhance the husband's ego, and make each sexual experience far more exciting and enjoyable. If the husband is similarly trained, and both synchronize their movements for maximum mutual stimulation, then the sex act can achieve its ultimate aim.

(3) *Vaginal Contraction*—The vagina is a muscular pouch with a depth of approximately 2½ to 3½ inches, but is flexible enough to accommodate a male sex organ of almost any size. For many years it was recognized by noted authorities that some women experienced a deep vaginal orgasm which was much more satisfying than the intense but rather short clitoric orgasm. Sometimes these were simultaneous, but other times one followed the other, with the vaginal

orgasm usually taking longer. It is estimated that fewer than 10 percent of wives have ever experienced a deep vaginal orgasm.

As there was no way of measuring one or the other, and since all reports were subjective, given by the wives themselves, it was difficult to assess the matter with scientific objectivity. This led to disagreements among some authorities and a reluctance to accept the existence of vaginal orgasm regardless of what the wives themselves felt or reported.

Then Dr. Arnold Kegel, a noted gynecologist who introduced exercise therapy to remedy some negative conditions invariably associated with flabbiness of the pubococcygeus, or vaginal muscle, discovered an important fact. Not only did strengthening of the vaginal muscle eliminate the original complaints, but it also led to *sexual feeling* in the vagina, and the resulting satisfaction helped many women to overcome their apathy toward, or dislike of, sexual intercourse.

Dr. Sarah R. Riedman says, "Even more surprising was his [Dr. Kegel's] discovery that as the patient improved there was increased sensory perception in the vagina. Women who previously were indifferent to sexual activity or regarded it with dissatisfaction began to experience gratification in the marital act." (*Heightening Sex Satisfaction,* Sex Education Library, Health Publications, New York, 1960)

The vaginal muscle, like all other muscles in the body, follows the natural law of use and disuse—lack of muscular activity leads to atrophy, which manifests itself by loss of muscle tone and increasing flabbiness accompanied by a progressive loss of strength, endurance, and neuromuscular coordination.

Drs. H. N. Martin and G. W. Fitz say, "A muscle long left unused diminishes in bulk and degenerates in quality, as is well seen when a muscle is paralyzed and remains permanently inactive." (*The Human Body,* Holt, Rinehart & Winston, Inc., New York, 1930)

Modern textbooks on physiology echo the same long-accepted law. Drs. L. H. Morehouse and A. T. Miller say, "Lack of use of muscles decreases the size of the fibers and increases the proportion of fat in the muscle tissues. The contractile strength of each fiber is diminished by disuse." (*Physiology of Exercise,* The C. V. Mosby Co., St. Louis, 1959)

There is practically no conscious use of the vaginal muscle. About the only time any effort is made to contract it is when one is caught short and attempts to "hold in" a full bladder or a menstrual flow.

To reeducate flabby vaginal muscles, Dr. Arnold Kegel invented a device known as a *perineometer,* a rubber cylinder with a pressure gauge attached to it, which is inserted into the vagina. The patient lies on her back and makes a conscious effort to contract her vaginal muscles. The strength of the muscular contractions is indicated on the gauge.

Considerable practice is required before there is even the slightest contraction, but gradually the muscle comes under conscious control, and the contractions get stronger and stronger.

Dr. Nadina R. Kavinoky, a practicing gynecologist, reports using a "well-lubricated Pyrex centrifuge 'test' tube." She says, "In order to relieve any anxiety the bride is then taught to relax and contract the vaginal muscles." ("Premarital Medical Examination," *Journal of the American Medical Association,* October, 1954)

Gradually we are discovering something that we have known all along about muscular efficiency and proving the existence of vaginal sensitivity and satisfying vaginal orgasm. Wives can do a great deal to heighten their own sexual enjoyment and that of their husbands by developing strong vaginal muscle control.

Many of the exercises to be described are aimed directly or indirectly at activating and strengthening the vaginal muscle. However, deliberate, voluntary control over this muscle can come only from planned, conscious, systematic exercise. For best results you are advised to make many conscious efforts to contract your vaginal muscle. At least one hundred efforts should be made each day in groups of ten or fifteen consecutive repetitions. The short practice sessions can be done standing, sitting, or lying down and may be performed at any time of the day or night. Since there is no visible action involved, they may be performed in public as well as private.

Until mental contact is established with your vaginal muscles you are advised to practice these contractions in the privacy of your own bedroom free from all distractions. This will enable you to *think* yourself into your vaginal muscle and *will* it to contract. If you have ever tried to activate unused muscles you will know how important such mental concentration is. Patients striving to recover the use of an injured limb after long disuse work harder mentally than physically. It has truly been said that thought is the mother of action. You must "think-and-do" to activate your vaginal muscle and must practice over and over again to establish satisfactory neuromuscular control.

It is not necessary to insert anything into the vagina to develop this control, and you are advised against doing so except under medical guidance. However, whenever you indulge in sexual intercourse, you should make a conscious effort to grip your partner's penis with your vagina by forcefully contracting and relaxing your vaginal muscle. At first there will be little noticeable difference for either of you, but as your vaginal gripping power increases, so too will your mutual sex sensitivity. This will increase the sexual satisfaction of both yourself and your mate.

By developing your sexual skills so that you can participate actively in the sex act, increase labial pressures at will, expose your clitoris to maximum stimulation, control your vaginal contractions, and synchronize your actions to those of your partner, you will soon begin to enjoy a more complete sexual fulfillment.

CHAPTER 4

HELPFUL SEX TRAINING ADVICE

TRAINING ADVICE

Before starting on your sexercise program, read this chapter carefully. It will show you what to do, how to do it, when to do it, and what each sexercise is meant to accomplish. Detailed instructions accompany each exercise. All exercises are fully illustrated. Even the untrained person who has never done any formal exercise before should have no difficulty following this very simple, yet very effective, specialized exercise program.

HOW MANY EXERCISES YOU SHOULD DO

At your first practice session do only two exercises from each section as follows:

> Warm-up and Flexibility
> Pelvic Thrust
> Gluteal Squeeze
> Thigh Rotation
> Thigh Adduction

Trunk Flection
Trunk Extension
Sexometrics

This will give you a total of 16 different exercises, all
aimed at the development of strength, stamina, skill, and
neuromuscular control in some of the most important, yet
most neglected, muscles in your entire body.

At your first practice session repeat each exercise only
four or five times. Take it easy—especially if you have not
done any exercise for some time and are not in good
physical condition.

At your second practice session you may add a few
more repetitions to each set of the same 16 different exercises.

At your third practice session, do two sets of four or five
repetitions of each exercise with a short rest between the
two sets. In other words, do the first exercise four or five
times in succession, take a short rest, and do the same exercise four of five more times in a row. Then go on to the
second exercise and repeat the process. Continue this right
down the line until you have done all 16 of the exercises.

HOW TO SELECT YOUR EXERCISES AND CHANGE YOUR PROGRAM

It really does not matter which two exercises you select
from each section to make up your starting program. However, to simplify things, you may take the first two exercises
from each section and do these as instructed for the first
three practice sessions.

At the beginning of your fourth practice session drop
three of the original exercises and pick up three new ones,
each from a different section. At the beginning of your fifth
practice session drop three more of the original exercises
and pick up three more new ones, again, each from a different section, Continue doing this until you have finally
dropped all the original 16 starting exercises.

By this time you will be sufficiently familiar with enough
different exercises to select them as you see fit. If you so
desire, you may continue the same procedure, dropping

the three oldest exercises each practice session and picking up three new ones in their place. This simple procedure could be continued until you have performed every exercise in the book.

After five or six practice sessions you may want to add more exercises to your training program. This will depend upon your physical condition, your response to the program you are doing, and your needs. If you find that 16 exercises are too easy for you then by all means add more. This is a matter which you, better than anyone else, can decide.

SETS AND REPETITIONS

All exercises in this book are described in terms of "sets" and "repetitions." It is important that you understand the meanings of these words, since they will be used often.

Repetition: When you perform an exercise *once,* this is called *one repetition.* If you do the same exercise twice in succession this is called two repetitions. If you do the same exercise three times in succession this is called three repetitions, and so on.

Set: A group of repetitions of the same exercise is called a *set.* Thus, if you do an exercise five times in succession and then stop for a rest, you will have performed one set of five repetitions of that exercise.

If you do an exercise five times in succession, stop for a rest, and do it five more times in succession, you will have done two sets of five repetitions of that exercise.

Practical Application: If your instructions call for you to do "two sets of five repetitions" of an exercise, you will repeat that exercise five times in succession, take a short rest, and then repeat the same exercise five more times in succession.

HOW OFTEN TO EXERCISE

In order to obtain and maintain the highest possible degree of total physical fitness it is strongly recommended by authorities that one should participate in at least one hour of planned physical activity every day. However, we are primarily interested in developing strength, stamina, endurance, flexibility, and neuromuscular coordination in certain body parts and muscle groups which are important to the satisfactory performance of the sex act. We recognize the vital importance of health and overall physical fitness. We know that a firm, trim, attractive female figure and a handsome masculine physique can contribute to mutual admiration and stimulation. We are aware that every exercise described in this book has many different values. Nevertheless, our main purpose, a specific *sexercise* program, can be achieved with approximately three 15-minute exercise periods per week.

For best results you are advised to space your sexercise periods, allowing approximately one day's rest between sessions. This is especially important during the first two or three weeks when so many unused muscles will be seeing action for the first time.

At the start, it is better to do too little than too much, in order to give your body a chance to adjust itself to the new demands made upon it by your exercise program. After two or three practice sessions you will get to know what is best for you. To make the most rapid progress, you are advised to increase gradually the number of exercises, the severity of your exercise program, and the length of your practice sessions.

HOW EXERCISES SHOULD BE PERFORMED

(A) ISOTONIC EXERCISES
(Those with Movement)

Unless otherwise instructed, each exercise should be performed over a full range of movement. All major muscle groups in the body work in opposing groups. For example, one group of muscles (flexors) bends your arm at the elbow, while an opposing group of muscles (extensors) straightens your arm. Thus, to exercise your arm muscles (primarily the biceps and triceps) fully, you must bend your arm as much as possible and then straighten it as much as possible. Likewise, inward rotators oppose outward rotators, pronators oppose supinators, adductors oppose abductors, and so forth.

Exercising from one extreme to the other helps to keep your ligaments, tendons, and muscles elastic, and guards against muscle shortening. Exercising over a full range of movement also gives the parts involved more flexibility and a greater scope of useful action.

All isotonic (movement) exercises in this book should be performed in a smooth, moderately paced, rhythmical manner. Jerky movements should be avoided. An appropriate musical background can be helpful as well as enjoyable.

(B) ISOMETRIC EXERCISES
(Those with No Movement)

To convert any isotonic exercise to an isometric exercise you simply *hold* each extreme position of the isotonic exercise for ten counts (approximately six seconds). In other words, you force the moving part as far as it will go in one direction, hold for ten counts, then force it as far as it will go in the opposite direction, and hold for another ten counts. Then go on to the next exercise and repeat the same process.

HOW TO BREATHE WHILE EXERCISING

No special breathing is required to perform any of the exercises in this book. Nature will take care of your breathing needs if you give her a chance. Do not hold your breath during any of the exercises. Just breathe naturally. The harder you exercise, the more deeply, strongly, and rapidly you will breathe. Your breathing will automatically adjust itself to your increased oxygen needs with no conscious effort on your part.

HOW LONG TO REST AFTER EACH SET OF EXERCISES

A short rest should be taken after the completion of each set of exercises. For example, if you do two sets of five repetitions of an exercise, you will do the exercise five times in succession, take a short rest, do the exercise five more times in succession and take another short rest.

Thirty seconds should be sufficient rest after one set of five repetitions of all but the most strenuous exercises described in this book. If you feel that you require more, then by all means take it. However, once you get warmed up, it is a good idea to keep your muscles warmed up, so do not let your "after-set" rest periods last more than a minute at a time.

BEST TIME OF DAY TO EXERCISE

Studies show that one may exercise at any time of the day or night provided it does not interfere with regular meals or regular sleeping hours. Select the time that suits you best and try to keep to this. Regularity is important in exercise because it is so easy to find other things to do and miss periods completely. Regular exercise periods are especially important during the first few weeks when your muscles will be learning entirely new coordinations.

EATING AND EXERCISING

It is not advisable to perform any strenuous exercise or participate in any vigorous activity for at least an hour after eating. Most athletes eat two or three hours before a competitive event and even then eat only a light meal.

If you indulge in any vigorous exertion when your stomach is full you may suffer stomach pains, cramps, or other discomforts. When your stomach is full, blood goes to your digestive organs to help them with their work. If you exert yourself physically at such a time, this blood will rush away from your digestive organs to your working muscles, thereby hindering or suspending digestion.

Most of the exercises described in this book cannot be

classed as strenuous, but some would be difficult to perform on a full stomach. Among these are the pelvic thrusts, the abdominal exercises, and the various trunk-bending exercises. Therefore it would be wise to wait for an hour after eating before doing any of these.

WHAT TO WEAR WHILE EXERCISING

No special clothing is required to perform any of the exercises described in this book. However, you may feel more comfortable in light, loose, porous clothing which permits ample free movement. Your exercise clothes should be changed frequently and kept as clean as possible. Some old pajamas or a full sweat suit make wonderful training clothes. In addition to giving you plenty of freedom, they can aid in keeping your muscles warm during your short rest periods. If possible, you should have two or three sets of exercise clothes so that one is always fresh and clean.

FINISH EACH EXERCISE PERIOD WITH A HOT SHOWER

After you finish each exercise period, treat yourself to a nice warm bath or a hot shower. Your body possesses more than two million tiny sweat glands which work extra hard when you are exercising. These glands help your body get rid of a multitude of poisonous wastes. If allowed to accumulate, these wastes may cause some skin disorders or offensive body odors.

Contrary to what you may hear, sweating is normal, natural, and beneficial. It must go on constantly, not only to get rid of nitrogenous wastes but also to regulate body temperature. A warm bath or hot shower, accompanied by soaping and scrubbing, not only helps your sweat glands finish their vital job but also feels great. Warm water has a relaxing effect on your muscles, stimulates surface circulation, and has a beneficial effect on your skin as a whole. A brisk total-body toweling after your shower will make your skin glow with radiant health, and make you feel good all over.

Cleanliness is extremely important to the enjoyable performance of the sex act and for happy marital relationships as a whole. Offensive odors can dampen or even destroy the most fervent ardor.

CHAPTER 5

WARM-UP AND
FLEXIBILITY EXERCISES

PRELIMINARY CONDITIONING

You are strongly advised to start each training session with a few "warm-up" and "flexibility" exercises. These are of great value in preparing your body for the more vigorous exercises to follow. "Cold" muscles have a greater resistance to change, have less elasticity, contract and relax more slowly, and must work harder than warm muscles. Cold muscles are weaker, have a lower blood supply, have a slower reaction time, and are inferior in neuromuscular coordination to warm muscles. Cold muscles are more vulnerable to stresses and strains, and suffer more aches and pains than warm muscles.

Warm-up exercises speed up respiration and circulation, bringing more oxygen to your blood and more blood to your working muscles. Your blood also carries energy supplies and building materials to your muscles, and takes away the poisonous waste products of metabolism. Warm-up exercises raise the internal temperature of your working muscles, lowering their viscosity and hence their resistance to change, thereby improving their overall efficiency.

Flexibility exercises not only contribute to the general warm-up but also improve the elasticity and tonicity of your ligaments, tendons, and muscles, thus enabling them to withstand greater stresses and strains.

39

Experienced athletes, coaches, and trainers, as well as physical education instructors know the value of warm-up and flexibility exercises. You cannot go wrong by following their lead in your own home training program.

ESPECIALLY FOR WARM-UP

Warm-up exercises call for big-muscle contractions such as those involved in running, jumping, and squatting. These will make you breathe more deeply and harder and will speed up your circulation quite rapidly. One or two of these before each regular practice session should be sufficient, although you may do more if you need the extra exercise. Examples are as follows:

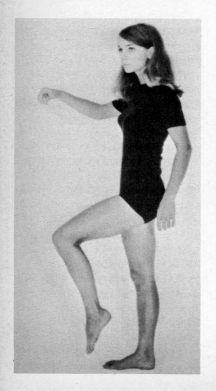

RUNNING IN PLACE

Stand erect with your arms bent across your chest. Start running in place slowly, barely lifting your feet off the floor. Gradually speed up your pace and lift your knees higher and higher in front of you. Pump your arms back and forth as you run. When your breathing becomes strong, gradually slow down and come to a stop.

ASTRIDE JUMPING WITH ARMS RAISING

Stand erect with your feet together and your arms hanging at your sides. Jump up and swing your arms to the sides. At the same time spread your feet and land on them in the astride position. Jump your feet together again and at the same time drop your arms to your sides. Repeat until your breathing becomes strong.

Note: The harder and higher you swing your arms and the faster you jump your feet apart and together, the more strenuous does this exercise become.

SQUAT THRUSTS

Stand erect with your feet apart and your arms hanging at your
sides. Squat down, bending your knees, and place both hands on
the floor with your feet between. Extend your legs backward as far
as they will go, straightening your knees and arching your back.
Jump both feet back to your hands so that you are in the squat
position again. Stand erect. Repeat until breathing becomes deeper
and stronger.

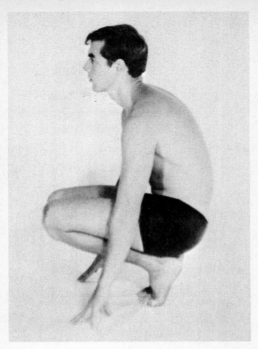

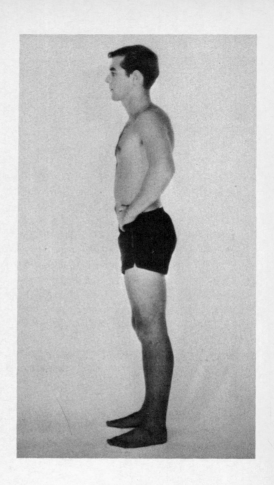

ALTERNATE THIGH HUGS

Stand erect with your feet comfortably apart and your hands on
your hips. Step diagonally right with your right foot, taking a long
step. Bend your trunk toward your right knee and wrap both arms
around your right thigh. Your left foot must not be moved. Return
to the starting position.

Take a long step diagonally left with your left foot. Bend your trunk toward your left knee and wrap both arms around your left thigh. This time your right foot must not be moved. Return to the erect standing position with your hands on your hips.

Repeat this exercise ten times, taking five long steps with each foot, or until breathing becomes deeper and stronger.

(Left) SEMI-SQUAT JUMPS

Stand erect with your left foot in front of your right foot. Place your hands behind your head. Lower your body about six inches by bending your knees. Spring straight up by straightening your knees and pushing off the floor with your toes. Change the position of your feet while in the air to land in a semi-squat position again, but this time with your right foot in front of your left foot. Continue these little squat jumps, changing feet with each jump, until your breathing speeds up.

ESPECIALLY FOR FLEXIBILITY

Flexibility exercises call for stretching, bending, twisting, turning, and reaching. They should commence very easily and lightly and gradually involve more and more stretch. They are usually done over the full range of muscular action, that is, from full extension to full flection. One or two of these, done as part of your preliminary warm-up prior to each regular practice session, should be sufficient. However, you may do more if you feel that you need the extra exercise. Examples are as follows:

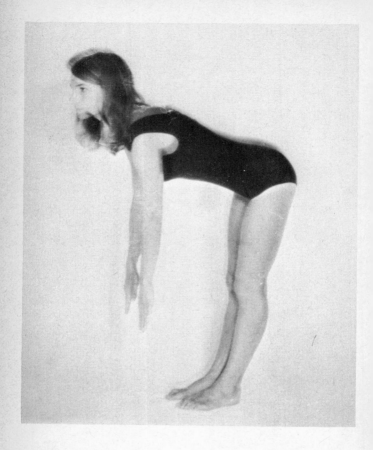

TRUNK BENDING FORWARD AND BACKWARD

Stand erect with your feet apart and your arms hanging at your sides. Bend your trunk forward, keeping your arms and knees straight. Try to touch the floor with your hands. Straighten your trunk, drop your shoulders back, arch your back, and reach down and back with your hands. Repeat five times, trying to reach farther down and farther back on each repetition. Take a short rest, and perform the same exercise five more times.

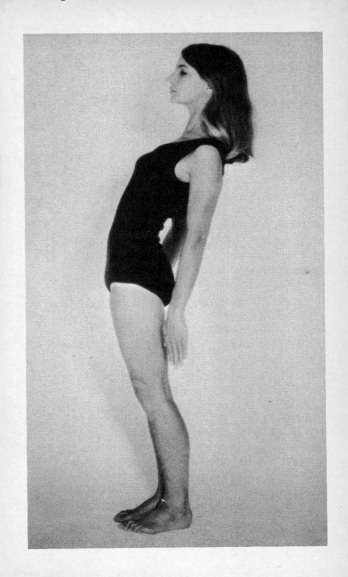

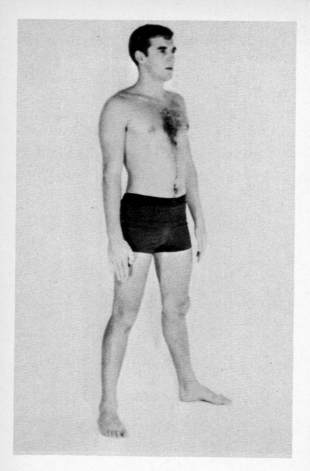

HEELS RAISING WITH ARMS SWINGING

Stand erect with your feet apart and your arms hanging at your sides. Keeping your arms straight, swing them outward and upward as far as they will go. At the same time rise up on your toes as high as you can go. Return to starting position. Repeat, trying to swing arms higher, raise heels higher, and arch back more on each succeeding repetition. Do two sets of five repetitions of this exercise with a short rest between.

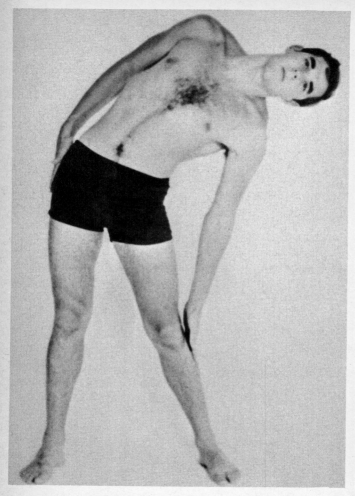

TRUNK BENDING FROM SIDE TO SIDE
Stand erect with your feet apart and arms hanging at your sides.
Bend to your left, reaching down your left leg with your left
hand. Bend to your right, reaching down your right leg with your
right hand. Repeat, going from one side to the other and trying
to reach farther down each time. Do two sets of five repetitions
of this exercise with a short rest between.

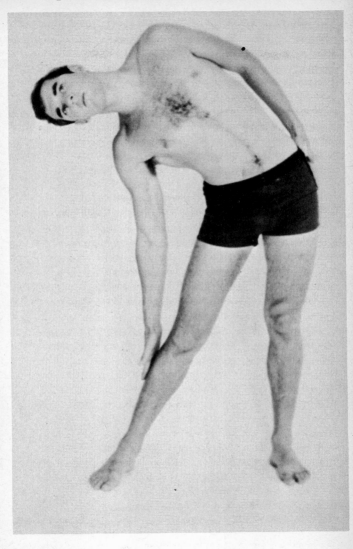

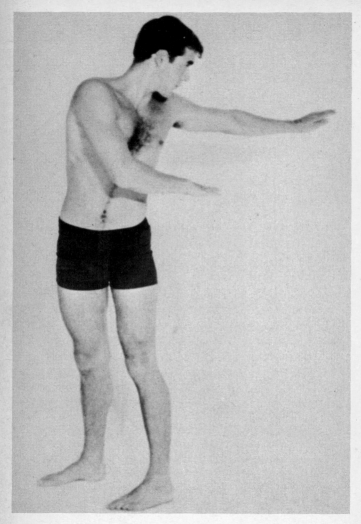

TRUNK TURNING WITH ARMS FLINGING

Stand erect with your feet apart and your arms bent across your
chest. Turn your trunk to the left, and at the same time fling your
left arm back as far as it will go. Turn your trunk to the right,

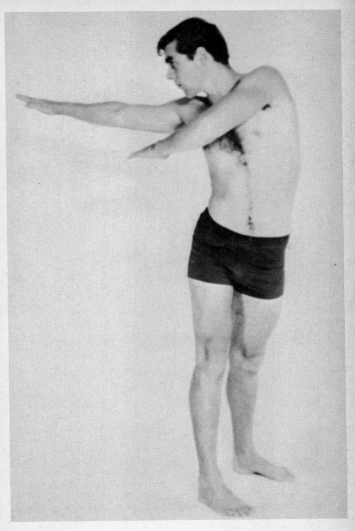

and at the same time fling your right arm back as far as it will go. Repeat, turning your trunk farther and flinging your arms harder each time. Do two sets of five repetitions of this exercise with a short rest between.

TRUNK BENDING WITH ALTERNATE TOE-TOUCHING

Stand erect with your feet apart and your arms outstretched at
shoulder level. Keeping your knees stiff, bend your trunk forward
and touch your right hand to your left toes. At the same time turn
your head to the left and swing your left arm as far back as it will
go. Return to starting position. Keeping your knees and arms stiff,

bend your trunk forward and touch your left hand to your right toes. At the same time turn your head to the right and swing your right arm as far back as it will go. Repeat, trying to turn your head and swing your free arm harder each time. Do two sets of five repetitions of this exercise with a short rest between.

KNEELING TRUNK-BEND FORWARD

Kneel on the floor. Sit back on your heels. Bend forward at the
waist as far as possible. Slide the backs of your hands on the floor
besides your feet and place your face on the floor. Raise trunk to
starting position again. Repeat, doing two sets of five repetitions
with a short rest after each set.

KNEELING TRUNK-BEND BACKWARD

Kneel on the floor. Place your hands on your hips. Bend back slowly. Straighten up again. Repeat, bending back a little more each time. When strong stretch is felt in hips, thighs, and back, take a short rest. Repeat three times.

KNEELING FOREARM REST WITH ROCKING ACTION

Kneel on floor. Bend forward and place your forearms on the floor in front of you. While in this position rock backward and forward as far as possible. Perform two sets of five repetitions with a short rest between sets.

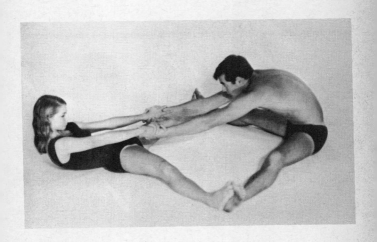

SEATED PARTNER PULLING STRETCH

Sit on floor facing your partner. Spread your legs far apart. Let your feet touch your partner's feet, and reach across and grasp your partner's wrists. Keeping your knees stiff and maintaining your

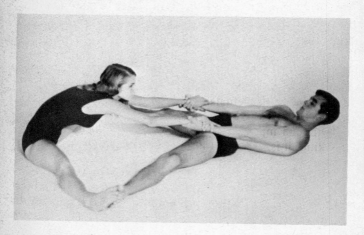

wrist grip throughout the exercise, bend forward and backward as far as you can. With each repetition of this exercise try to bend farther forward and backward until you can touch your back to the floor while still holding hands. Perform two sets of five repetitions with a short rest between sets.

CHAPTER 6

THE VITALLY
IMPORTANT PELVIC
THRUST

THE PELVIC THRUST

There is perhaps no action which is more important to the satisfactory performance of the sex act than *pelvic thrust*. If any sex movement can be considered natural or instinctive it is this. The entry of the male organ depends upon this action, and the subsequent stimulation of both the male and the female sex organs depends largely upon a continuation of the same thrusting action.

Although many females lie passively with no action of any kind, it is highly unlikely that there are any males who do not at least thrust backward and forward with their pelvic region during the sex act. In spite of this, it is doubtful that many males have had any training which would make for skillful pelvic thrusting. The same applies to females, only more so. To make things worse, there are no actions in modern life which involve these movements, thus there is no carry-over from any other activity.

Thrusting backward and forward with the pelvic area is almost exclusively limited to the act of sexual intercourse. It more specifically applies to males, since the vast majority of women lack the strength, stamina, flexibility, and neuromuscular coordination needed for pelvic movements.

Automation and mechanization have not only led to overall physical deterioration in man but also to less walking and more sitting, which has resulted in a gradually decreasing flexibility in the pelvic area. Not only do we sit most of the day at work, but we sit traveling to and from work, and spend most of our leisure time sitting—watching TV, movies, sports, plays, or driving around in our cars. As a result, the muscles of the pelvic region not only lack strength, stamina, power, and tonus, but also lack flexibility and neuromuscular coordination. With decreasing activity and increasing age our pelvic regions become less and less capable of functioning efficiently. To aggravate this negative condition still more, most women and many men wear restricting girdles which inhibit what little natural movement is left. Such tight foundation garments interfere with normal circulation, and permit weak muscles to become still weaker.

In the pelvic region, human beings are getting progressively weaker. We receive no instruction in *how* to move our pelvic area for maximum sex participation, stimulation, and satisfaction. Up to now there has been no deliberately planned, regular, systematic neuromuscular *training* for the vitally important act of sexual intercourse.

Pelvic control is especially important to the ever-increasing number of wives who do not experience full sexual satisfaction through orgasm—to passive wives, to wives who resist their husbands, to wives who do not enjoy the sex act, to frigid wives, and to wives who actually dislike sexual intercourse. It is important because active physical participation helps to remove such mental and emotional inhibitions. Most important of all, pelvic control enables the wife to expose her clitoris to maximum stimulation during the sex act, thereby assuring her of an intensely enjoyable and highly satisfying clitoric orgasm.

The exercises that follow are designed to strengthen the muscles of the pelvic girdle and give them more stamina; to give the ligaments, tendons, and muscles more flexibility; and to increase the speed, range, variety, and intensity of various sex movements. They are designed to develop the neuromuscular control which will enable both partners to obtain the highest possible degree of mutually satisfying sex stimulation.

SPECIAL INSTRUCTIONS

When practicing any of the exercises given in this section *"think, visualize, and do."* Try to see and feel the actions involved. This will help to create connections between mind and unused muscles where none exist or strengthen weak connections that do exist. At first, some of the actions may feel impossible to perform, but with persistent practice more and more control will develop.

Wives are reminded that vaginal contraction is vitally important to the satisfactory performance of the sex act, and are urged to combine this action whenever possible with the pelvic thrust. In most cases this will be easier to do at the end or beginning of the thrust but may also be done throughout the full range of the thrust.

Husbands are urged to make a conscious effort to lift the penis through muscular contraction at the forward end of each thrust. Even though the movement is small, the pulsating action resulting from the alternate contractions and relaxations of the penis simulate ejaculatory contractions which bring about orgasmic reactions on the part of many wives. Authorities do not agree on the reasons for this female response. Some believe that the muscular contractions of the male penis during orgasm trigger a like reaction from the female through tactile sensitivity of the vagina. Others believe that the psychological reasons are predominant—the wife knows that she has been successful in bringing her husband an intensely enjoyable climax, and this releases her own inhibitions. Whatever the cause, the result is the same—more complete sexual satisfaction for both partners.

MAXIMUM PELVIC CONTROL

The following exercises have been especially designed to give you the greatest possible control over your entire pelvic area. They will give you the neuromuscular coordination which you need to move your sex organ region backward, forward, sideward, upward, downward, obliquely, clockwise, counterclockwise, or any combination thereof.

These exercises have been designed to give you maximum control of this area regardless of the position of your body, so that you can move this area in a multitude of different ways under a variety of different conditions.

With a reasonable amount of practice you should be able to perform any movement or combinations of movements you desire at varying speeds ranging from very slow to very fast, and at varying intensities ranging from gentle to vigorous for varying durations of time.

It is impossible to overestimate the tremendous value of pelvic control to both partners in the satisfactory performance of the sex act. No other action is more natural, regardless of the position you and your partner may assume. No other action contributes more to the labial, clitoric, and deep vaginal stimulation of the female; nor to the physical and psychological enjoyment of the male, thus helping to achieve the ultimate in sexual pleasure for both partners. If you did no other exercises in this book but these, your sexual ability and agility would be improved considerably.

ISOTONIC (MOVEMENT) EXERCISES COME FIRST

Every exercise described in this chapter is isotonic, because movement is important to the pelvic thrust. It is important that you get all the movement possible for each exercise described—going from one extreme of movement to the other—and always striving to increase the range of action. Each exercise in this chapter should be done with movement first.

Only after you have done every exercise isotonically

(with movement) should you go back and perform them all again isometrically (without movement). When performing each exercise isometrically, be sure to go as far as possible in one direction and *hold* for ten counts (approximately six seconds) and then go as far as possible in the opposite direction and *hold* for another ten counts.

EXERCISES FOR DEVELOPING PELVIC CONTROL

(A) FORWARD-UPWARD, DOWNWARD-BACKWARD ACTION

Though a number of different body positions are included in this group, all the pelvic actions are essentially

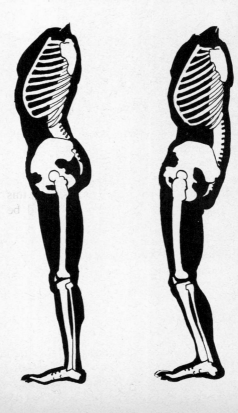

the same, namely up-forward and down-backward. These actions are especially important to the wife because they enable her to expose her clitoris to maximum stimulation, thereby bringing her the ultimate in sexual satisfaction. Through these actions she can exert considerable control over the sex act so far as she is concerned, even in cases where her partner is not so experienced. Obviously, if the husband also develops excellent pelvic control, and both partners synchronize their pelvic movements, they should be able to obtain the highest possible peak of mutual sexual stimulation and satisfaction.

To obtain the proper action required by this group of exercises, assume that your pelvis rotates on an axle which runs through the middle of your body from one hipbone to the other. Then, force your pelvis to rotate on this axle, first in a forward-upward manner, and then in a downward-backward manner. For the forward-upward action, force your "s.o.r." (sex organ region) forward and upward as though you were an exotic dancer doing the "bumps." With each forward pelvic thrust, pull your stomach in to accentuate the action. For the downward-backward action, thrust your posterior backward and upward as if you were doing the "fanny bumps." At the same time hollow the small of your back to accentuate this action.

There is no better, simpler way of learning this very important pelvic thrusting, tilting, upward-downward, rotating action than by doing it with your back against a wall as described below. Once mastered in this upright back-to-wall manner, the same action can easily be applied to all the other exercises listed in this group.

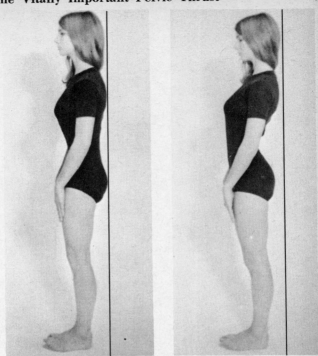

ERECT, STANDING WITH BACK AGAINST WALL

Stand erect, feet together, and with your heels, buttocks, and back of the head pressed against a wall. Pull in your stomach, force your s.o.r. forward and upward, slide your buttocks down the wall, and try to press the small of your back against the wall. This will give you the correct forward-upward pelvic tilting action. To reverse this action, hollow the small of your back, and slide your buttocks up the wall as high as possible. This will give you the correct downward-backward action. Now alternate, going first in one direction and then in the other, each time striving to get the greatest possible range of movement. Start slowly, and gradually speed up the action.

Do two sets of four or five repetitions at your first training session with a short rest between sets. Gradually add more repetitions to each set at subsequent practices until you can do fifty or more with ease.

Variation: Perform the same exercise with feet spread apart.

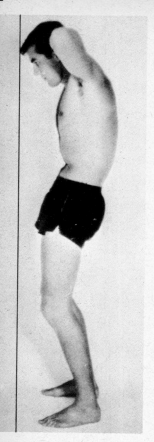 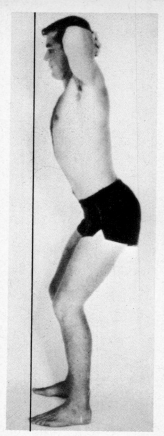

ERECT, STANDING WITH FRONT AGAINST WALL

Stand erect, feet together, and with your toes and chest pressed against a wall. Force your s.o.r. up the wall as far as possible, and then force it down the wall as far as possible. Alternate from one extreme to the other, constantly striving to increase the range of motion. The action is exactly the same as that described on page 71 except that you are facing toward the wall instead of away from it. Do two sets of repetitions with a short rest between, and gradually increase the number of repetitions at subsequent practice sessions.

Variation: Perform the same exercise with feet spread apart.

ERECT, STANDING AWAY FROM WALL

Stand erect, feet together, away from the wall. Now repeat all of the instructions given in first exercise above.

Variation: Perform the same exercise with feet spread apart.

HALF SQUAT WITH FEET APART

Stand erect with your feet spread apart. Lower body to half-squat position by bending your knees. Stay in this position while you perform the pelvic thrusting, tilting, and rotating action as described in first exercise.

SITTING, HANDS ON FLOOR

Sit on the floor, stretching your legs in front of you and placing
the palms of your hands on the floor just behind your hips. Perform pelvic action as instructed in first exercise.

Variation: Perform the same exercise with legs spread apart.

Variation: Perform the same exercise with knees bent, feet on
floor.

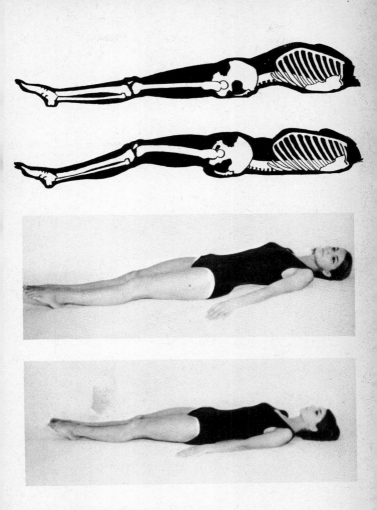

BACK-LYING WITH KNEES STRAIGHT

Lie on your back on the floor with your legs together and knees straight, arms alongside the body with palms on floor. Perform pelvic action as instructed in first exercise.

Variation: Perform the same exercise with legs spread apart.

BACK-LYING WITH KNEES BENT

Lie on your back on the floor with knees together and bent, feet
flat on the floor, arms above the head with palms up. Perform
pelvic action as described in first exercise.

Variation: Perform the same exercise with feet spread apart.

BACK-LYING, KNEES BENT, BUTTOCKS RAISED OFF FLOOR

Lie on your back on the floor with knees together and bent, feet
flat on floor. Raise buttocks off the floor and keep them off floor
until the exercise is finished. Place arms alongside the body with
palms on floor. Perform pelvic action as instructed in first exercise.
Variation: Perform the same exercise with feet spread apart.

BACK-LYING WITH BODY ARCHED

Lie on your back on the floor with feet together and arms alongside the body, palms on floor. Keeping shoulders, head, arms,
hands, and heels on floor, arch body strongly so that buttocks and
rest of body lift off the floor. Holding this strongly arched position
perform pelvic action as described in first exercise.

Variation: Perform the same exercise with feet spread apart.

SIDE-LYING WITH KNEES STRAIGHT

Lie on your left side, with legs and body straight. Place right hand
on floor in front of chest to help you maintain balance. Holding
this position, perform pelvic action as described in first exercise.

Variation: Perform the same exercise with knees bent.

Variation: Perform both of the above exercises lying on your
right side.

FRONT-LYING WITH ARMS EXTENDED

Lie face down on the floor with legs together, arms extended beyond head, palms on the floor. Perform the pelvic action as described in first exercise.

Variation: Perform the same exercise with legs spread apart.

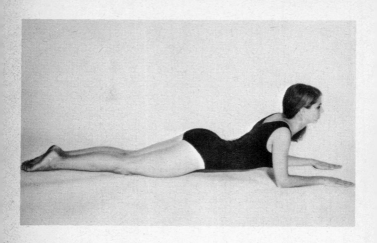

FRONT-LYING, RESTING WEIGHT ON FOREARMS

Lie face down on the floor with legs together. Bend your elbows, and place your forearms and the palms of your hands on the floor beneath your chest. Raise upper body so that chest does not touch floor. Perform pelvic action as described in first exercise.

Variation: Perform the same exercise with legs spread apart.

FRONT-LEANING REST

Lie face down on floor with legs together. Keeping body stiff, place hands on floor beside chest. Stiffen body and push up off floor until arms are straight. Only the toes and the palms of the hands should be touching the floor. This is the popular "push-up." Holding this "front-leaning rest" position, perform the pelvic action as instructed in first exercise.

Variation: Perform the same exercise with legs spread apart.

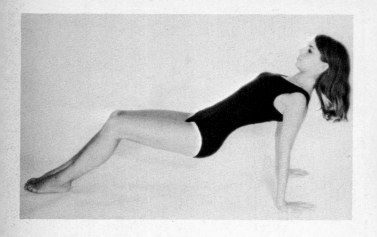

BACK-LEANING REST

Sit on the floor with legs together. Place hands on floor behind
buttocks. Raise buttocks high up from floor and lean head back.
Body should be straight, and weight of body should be resting only
on your heels and your hands. Holding this position, perform the
pelvic action as described in first exercise.

Variation: Perform the same exercise with legs spread apart.

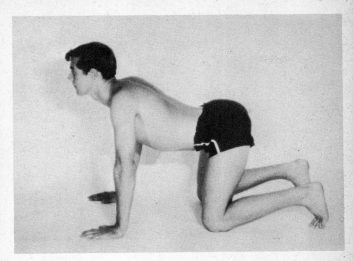

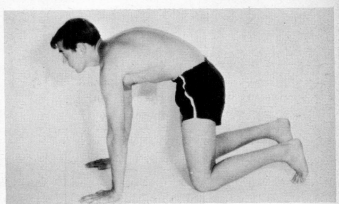

FRONT-KNEELING REST

Kneel on floor. Bend forward and place both hands on the floor, then move them forward about ten inches so your upper body is leaning forward. Holding this position, perform the pelvic action as instructed in first exercise.

Variation: Perform the same exercise with legs spread apart.

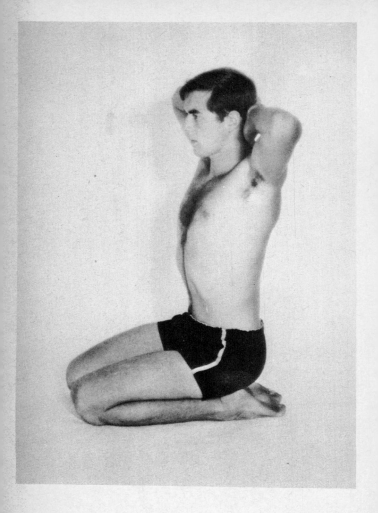

SITTING BACK ON LEGS

Kneel down on the floor on both knees. Sit back on your legs so that your buttocks touch your heels. While in this position, perform the pelvic action as described in first exercise.

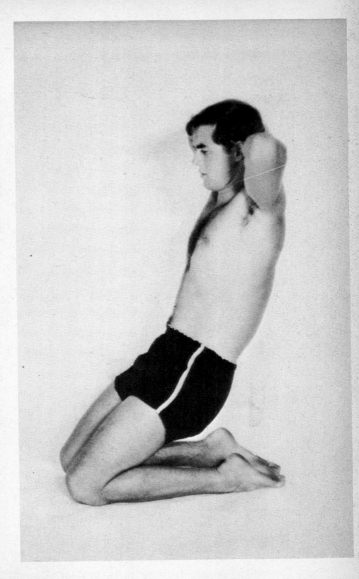

KNEELING WITH TRUNK ERECT

Kneel down on both knees, keeping your trunk in an erect position. Perform the pelvic action, while kneeling, as described in first exercise.

SITTING ON EDGE OF CHAIR

Sit on edge of chair. Reach back with the hands and grasp the sides of the chair. While in this position, perform the pelvic action as described in first exercise.

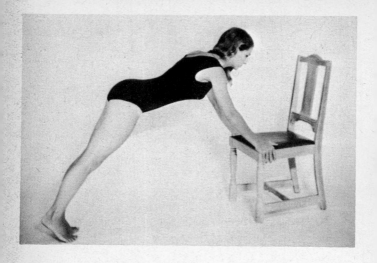

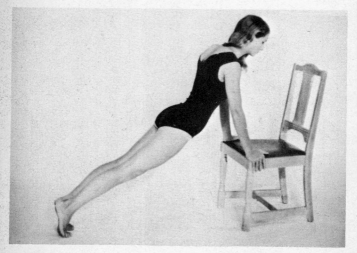

FRONT-LEANING REST WITH HANDS ON CHAIR

Stand about three feet away from a chair, facing it. Lean forward and place your hands on the chair. While holding this position, perform the pelvic action as described in first exercise.

BACK-LEANING REST WITH HANDS ON CHAIR

Stand about two feet away from a chair, facing away from it. Lean back and place your hands on the chair. Holding this position, perform the pelvic action as instructed in first exercise.

(B) SIDE-TO-SIDE ACTION

The body positions in this section are exactly the same as the body positions described in (A) above. Only the action is different. Therefore, the basic instructions are the same. In other words, you assume the same positions in exactly the same way as in (A). However, this time, instead of the thrust being essentially forward and backward, it is specifically from one side to the other. In the side-to-side action you thrust your hips to the left and then to the right, going from one extreme to the other. As far as possible your legs and your upper body should remain still while your pelvic region moves from side to side.

To get the correct action required for this group of exercises, assume that you are standing between two upright posts with about seven inches between your hips and the posts at either side. Keeping legs and upper body as still as possible, thrust left hip at left post, then right hip at right post. You can get the same action by standing in an open doorway and thrusting your hips from side to side as though trying to touch them to each side of the door jamb. The same action applies regardless of whether you are sitting, standing, kneeling, lying, or in any other position.

This side-to-side thrust, though not as important as the front-back tilting thrust, is far less commonly used by either males or females, and therefore the muscles involved are weaker. Not only does this movement have value in itself, providing more variety to the sex act, but it also contributes greatly to overall pelvic region flexibility and control. Again start with two sets of four or five repetitions until you can do fifty with ease.

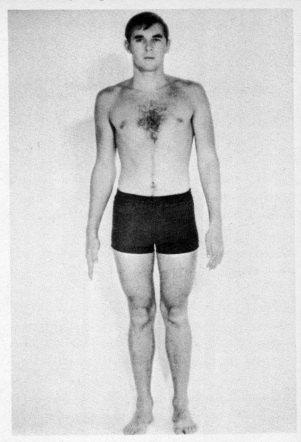

ERECT, STANDING WITH BACK AGAINST WALL

Stand erect, feet normal, with your heels, buttocks and back of head pressing against a wall. Slide buttocks to your left and then to your right. Pretend you are standing between two posts, and are trying to touch them alternately with your left and right hip.

Do two sets of four or five repetitions at your first training session, with a short rest between sets. Gradually add more repetitions to each set at subsequent practices until you can do fifty or more with ease. Follow the same procedure for all the other exercises in this section.

Variation: Perform the same exercise with feet spread apart.

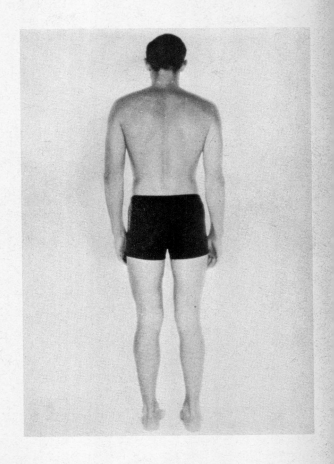

ERECT, STANDING WITH FRONT TO WALL

This exercise is done exactly like the first one except that you are facing the wall.

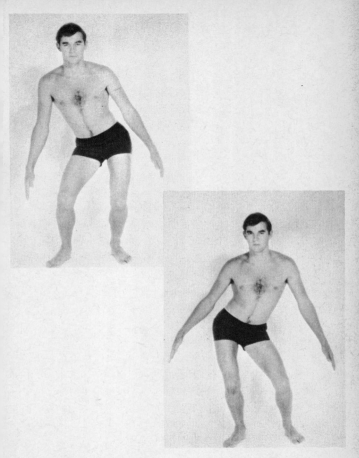

HALF-SQUAT WITH FEET APART

Stand erect with feet apart. Squat halfway down. Hold this position as you force your hips from left to right as in first exercise.

← ERECT, STANDING AWAY FROM WALL

This exercise is done exactly as the first except that you stand away from the wall.

SITTING, HANDS ON FLOOR

Sit on floor with legs stretched in front and hands on floor beside buttocks. Slide buttocks to left and right alternately.

Variation: Perform the same exercise with legs apart.

BACK-LYING WITH KNEES STRAIGHT

Lie back on floor with legs together and knees straight, arms
alongside body. Slide buttocks to left and right alternately.
   Variation: Perform the same exercise with legs spread apart.

BACK-LYING WITH KNEES BENT

Lie back on floor with knees together and bent, feet flat on the floor, arms alongside body. Slide buttocks to left and right alternately.

Variation: Perform the same exercise with feet spread apart.

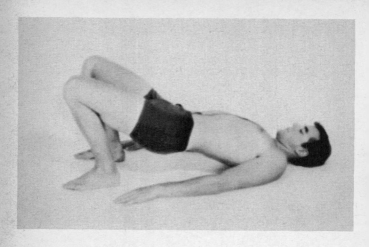

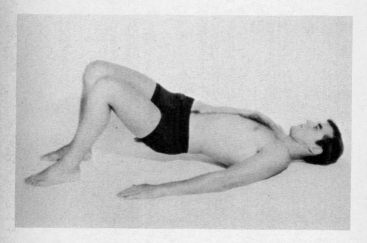

BACK-LYING, KNEES BENT, BUTTOCKS OFF FLOOR

Lie back on floor with knees together and bent, feet flat on floor, arms alongside body. Raise buttocks off floor, and keep off floor until exercise is finished. Thrust hips alternately to the left and the right.

Variation: Perform the same exercise with feet spread apart.

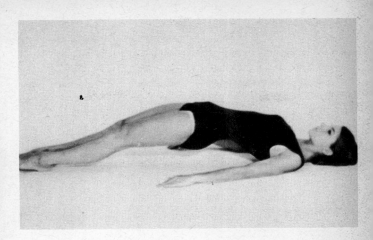

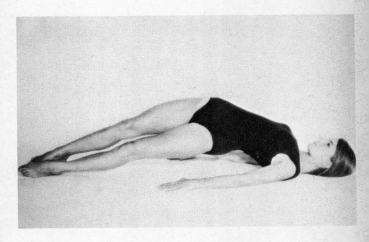

BACK-LYING WITH BODY ARCHED

Lie back on floor with legs together and arms on floor alongside body. Keeping head, shoulders, arms, and heels on floor, arch body strongly so that buttocks and rest of body lift off the floor. Hold this position while thrusting your hips alternately to the left and right.

Variation: Perform the same exercise with legs spread apart.

SIDE-LYING WITH KNEES STRAIGHT

Lie on the left side with legs and body straight. Place right hand on floor in front of chest to help maintain balance. Holding this position, thrust pelvis up to the right and lower again. Continue action as advised in preceding exercise. Perform same exercise lying on your right side.

Variation: Perform the same exercise with knees bent.

FRONT-LYING WITH ARMS EXTENDED

Lie face down on floor with legs together, arms extended beyond head, and palms flat on the floor. Thrust hips alternately to the left and the right.

Variation: Perform the same exercise with legs spread apart.

FRONT-LYING, RESTING WEIGHT ON FOREARMS

Lie face down on floor with legs together. Bend your elbows and place forearms and the palms of your hands on the floor close to your chest. Raise upper body so that chest does not touch floor. Thrust hips alternately to the left and the right.

Variation: Perform the same exercise with legs spread apart.

FRONT-LEANING REST

Lie face down on the floor with legs together. Place palms of
hands on floor beside chest. Keeping body stiff, straighten arms
and raise chest off floor. Only your toes and the palms of your
hands should be touching the floor. This "front rest" position is
commonly known as a "push-up." Holding this position, thrust
hips alternately to the left and to the right.

Variation: Perform the same exercise with legs spread apart.

BACK-LEANING REST

Sit on floor with legs together. Place hands on floor behind buttocks. Raise buttocks as high as possible off the floor and lean head and shoulders back. Holding this position, thrust hips alternately to the left and to the right.

Variation: Perform the same exercise with legs spread apart.

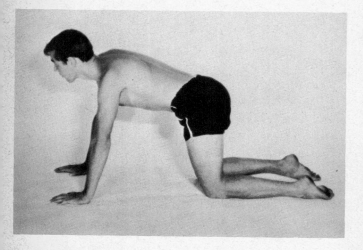

FRONT-KNEELING REST

Kneel on floor. Bend forward and place palms of hands on floor, and move them forward about ten inches so that your upper body is leaning forward. Holding this position, thrust your hips alternately to the left and to the right.

Variation: Perform the same exercise with the legs spread apart.

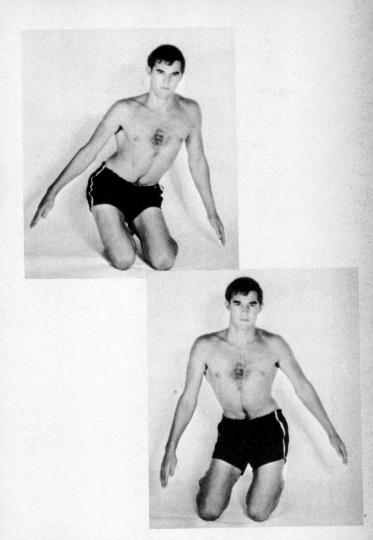

KNEELING WITH TRUNK ERECT

Kneel down on both knees, keeping your trunk in an erect position.
Thrust hips alternately to the left and to the right.

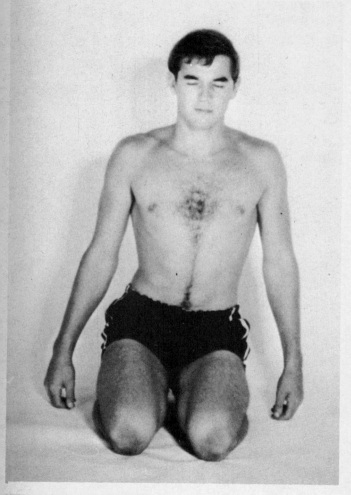

SITTING BACK ON THE LEGS

Kneel on the floor. Sit back so that your buttocks touch your heels. While in this position, thrust your hips alternately to the left and to the right.

SITTING ON EDGE OF CHAIR

Sit on edge of chair. Reach back with both hands and grasp the sides of the chair seat. While in this position, thrust hips alternately to the left and to the right.

FRONT-LEANING REST WITH HANDS ON CHAIR

Stand about two feet away from a chair, facing it. Lean forward and place your hands on the chair. While holding this position, thrust your hips alternately to the left and to the right.

BACK-LEANING REST WITH HANDS ON CHAIR

Stand about two feet away from a chair, facing away from it.
Lean back and place your hands on the chair. Holding this position, thrust your hips alternately to the left and to the right.

Special Note Re Sections (A) and (B): After you have done all the exercises in (A) and (B) separately and individually as described, you may combine both actions each time you assume each of the positions. For example, when performing the first exercise in this chapter you may do two sets of repetitions of the front-back action and then two sets of the side-to-side action. Then go on to the next exercise, and in the same manner perform the front-back action, and follow immediately with the side-to-side action. Thus you will be combining Sections (A) and (B) for all the different positions described.

*(C) CLOCKWISE AND
COUNTERCLOCKWISE ACTION*

The body positions in this section are exactly the same as the body positions described in (A) and (B) above. Only the action is different. Therefore the basic instructions are the same. In other words, you assume the same positions in exactly the same way as they are described in (A) and (B) above. However, this time, instead of thrusting forward and backward as in (A) or side-to-side as in (B), you will thrust first in a clockwise and then in a counterclockwise manner.

To perform the clockwise action, thrust your hips to the left, then forward, then to the right, then backward, and then to the left again, describing a complete circle like the hands of a clock. For the counterclockwise action, do the exact opposite, thrusting your hips to the right, then forward, then to the left, then backward, and then to the right again. This action is similar to that of the hands of a clock when you are turning them back.

The circular action of your "s.o.r." (sex organ region) is exactly the same as that used to make a hoola hoop circle around your waist. When performing each of the following exercises, imagine that you are actually trying to circle a hoola hoop just above your hips, first in one direction (clockwise) and then in the opposite direction (counterclockwise).

This action can contribute much to the stimulating pressures which can be exerted during the sexual act, thereby heightening the pleasure of both partners. It is especially valuable to the female who has difficulty reaching an orgasm.

For the following group of exercises, do one set of four or five repetitions clockwise, take a short rest, and then do a second set of repetitions counterclockwise. The same procedure should be followed for each of the exercises described. Gradually add more repetitions at subsequent practice sessions to each of these two sets until you can do fifty or more with ease.

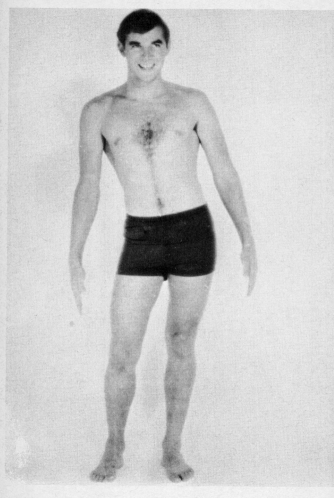

ERECT, STANDING AWAY FROM WALL

Stand erect with feet slightly apart. Move pelvic region clockwise
four or five times in succession, then reverse the action and
move it counterclockwise four or five times.

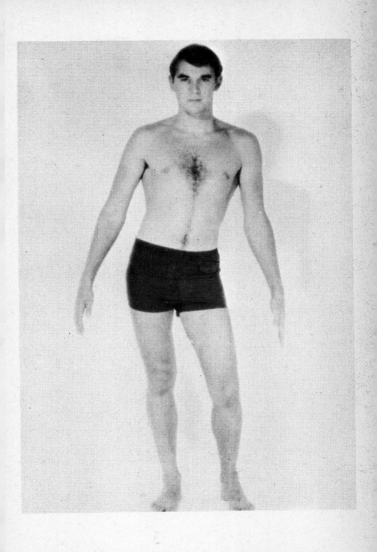

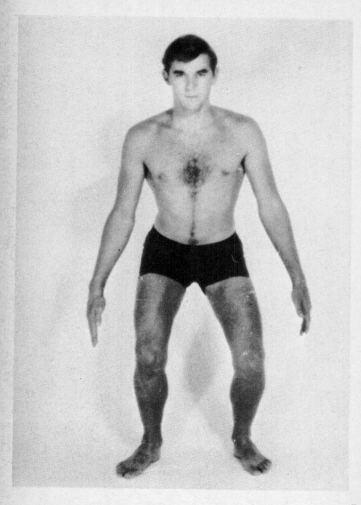

HALF-SQUAT WITH FEET APART

Stand erect, feet apart, and squat halfway down. Move pelvic region clockwise and then counterclockwise as instructed in first exercise.

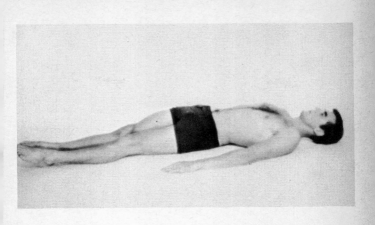

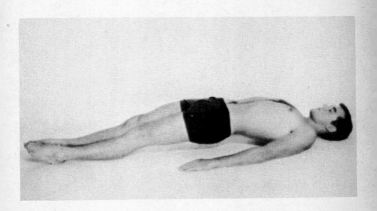

BACK-LYING WITH KNEES STRAIGHT

Lie on your back, legs together, knees straight, arms alongside body. Move pelvic region clockwise and then counterclockwise.

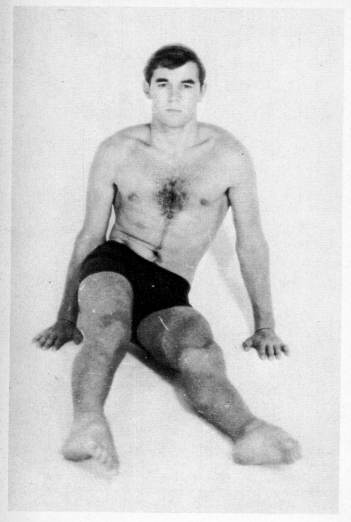

SITTING WITH FEET APART

Sit on floor with legs stretched and apart. Place hands on floor beside buttocks. Move pelvic region clockwise; then counterclockwise.

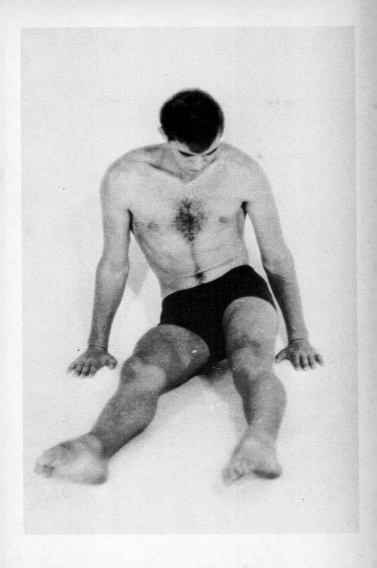

BACK-LYING WITH KNEES BENT

Lie back on floor with knees together and bent, feet flat on floor,
arms alongside body. Move pelvic region clockwise and then
counterclockwise.

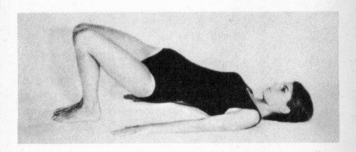

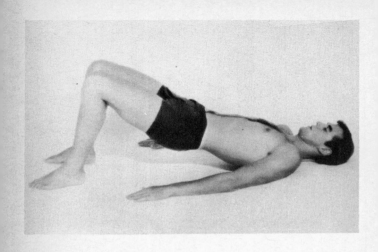

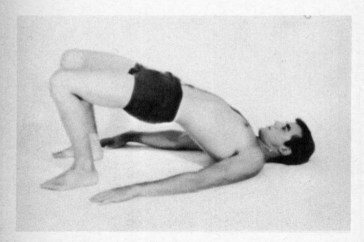

BACK-LYING, KNEES BENT, BUTTOCKS OFF FLOOR

Lie back on floor with knees bent, feet apart and flat on floor, and arms alongside body. Raise buttocks off floor and hold off floor until exercise is finished. Move pelvic region clockwise and then counterclockwise.

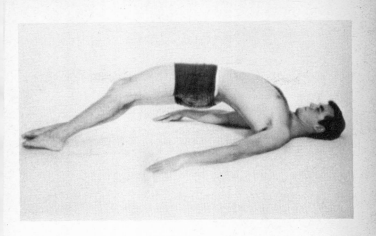

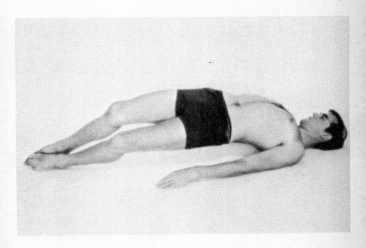

BACK-LYING WITH BODY ARCHED

Lie back on floor with legs apart and arms on floor alongside body. Keeping head, shoulders, arms, and heels on the floor, arch body strongly so that buttocks and rest of body lift off the floor. Hold this position while you move your pelvic region clockwise and then counterclockwise.

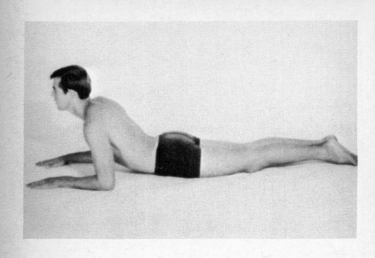

FRONT-LYING, RESTING WEIGHT ON FOREARMS

Lie face down on floor with legs slightly apart. Bend elbows, and place forearms and the palms of hands on the floor close to chest. Raise upper body so that chest does not touch the floor. Move pelvic region clockwise and then counterclockwise while holding this position.

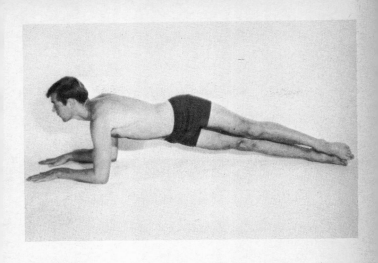

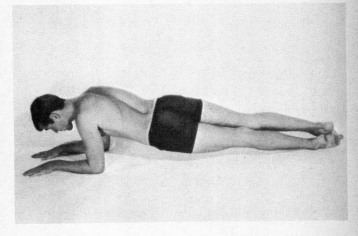

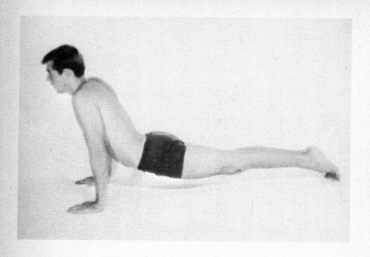

FRONT-LEANING REST

Lie face down on floor with legs slightly apart. Place palms of
hands on floor beside chest. Keeping body stiff, straighten arms
and raise chest off floor. Only your toes and the palms of your
hands should be touching the floor. Hold this "front rest" position
while you move your pelvic region clockwise then counterclockwise.

BACK-LEANING REST

Sit on floor with legs slightly apart. Place hand on floor behind buttocks. Raise buttocks as high as possible off floor, and lean head and shoulders back. Holding this position, move your pelvic region clockwise and then counterclockwise.

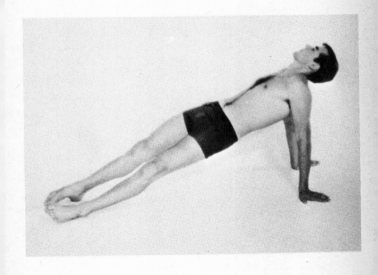

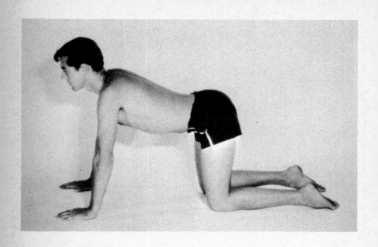

FRONT-KNEELING REST

Kneel on floor. Bend forward and place palms of hands on floor
and move them forward about ten inches so that your upper body
is leaning forward. Holding this position, move your pelvic region
clockwise and then counterclockwise.

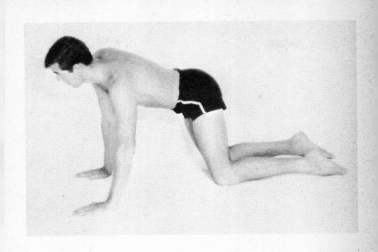

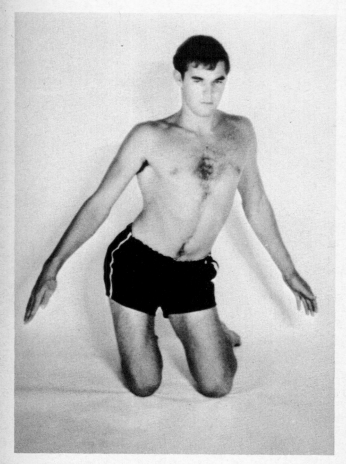

KNEELING WITH TRUNK ERECT

Kneel down on both knees, keeping your trunk in an erect position. Move your pelvic region clockwise and then counterclockwise.

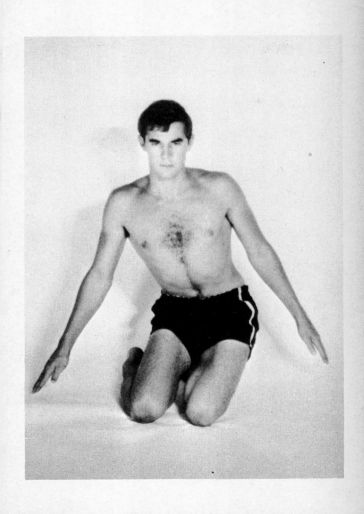

FRONT-LEANING REST WITH HANDS ON CHAIR

Stand erect about three feet away from a chair, facing it. Lean forward and place your hands on the chair. While holding this position, move your pelvic region clockwise and then counterclockwise.

BACK-LEANING REST WITH HANDS ON CHAIR

Stand about two feet away from a chair, facing away from it. Lean back and place your hands on the chair. Holding this position, move your pelvic region clockwise and then counterclockwise.

(D) ROTATING ACTIONS OF THE HIPS

This action calls for a twisting movement around a vertical axis running through the center line of the body. In other words, think of a rod running through the middle of your body from your head to your feet. Then, keeping your feet and your shoulders as still as possible, force your hips to rotate around this axis turning them as far to the left as possible and then as far to the right as possible. The action is very much the same as the "twist" dance except that the feet are not moved.

ERECT, STANDING "TWIST" ACTION

Stand erect with the feet slightly apart. Rotate hips as far as possible toward your left. Then rotate your hips as far as possible to your right as described above. Keep feet and shoulders as still as possible, forcing your hips and pelvic region as a whole to do all the moving. Do two sets of four or five repetitions with a short rest between sets at your first practice session. Gradually add more and more repetitions to each set until you can do fifty or more with ease.

Note: If you wish, you may try this same rotating (twist) action with other body positions mentioned in group (A).

CHAPTER 7

MORE SEX ENJOYMENT WITH THE GLUTEAL SQUEEZE

GLUTEAL EXERCISE

Gluteal control is very important to lovemaking. It enables you to move your s.o.r. (sex organ region) directly forward and backward by tensing and relaxing your buttocks.

Few people have even a modicum of gluteal control. Ballet dancers, however, are *taught* to tense and relax their gluteal muscles. If you studied ballet under an expert you will undoubtedly recall the "silver dollar" squeeze.

"Pull your cheeks together!" shouted the ballet master.

He was talking about your posterior cheeks, of course.

He probably slapped you on the derriere impersonally, even angrily, but to no avail. You still did not know what he was talking about or what you were supposed to do. Then out came the silver dollar.

If the experience was a little jolting and undignified, to say the least, you did learn more from it in three seconds than you could in three weeks with any other kind of instruction.

The silver dollar is pushed partway in from behind, and

automatically, instantaneously, you do exactly what you are supposed to do without a word of instruction—you draw your "cheeks" together and force your s.o.r. forward. But that is not all—you are now told to squeeze your gluteus maximus muscles together and to "hold" the silver dollar in place while you perform various ballet movements.

The purpose of all this is *control*. We too, are interested in control, but for other and far more important reasons. We want this highly specialized gluteal control so that both partners in the intimate sex act can participate fully to obtain the highest possible degree of mutual satisfaction and exhilarating joy.

Gluteal control is important to both husband and wife. If either partner possesses this control it means more pleasurable pressures for both in their sex organ regions. Control on the part of the male is important, not only for his own physical enjoyment, but for the satisfaction of the female, which also brings him psychological pleasure.

Control on the part of the female is even more important to her, because it is possible for her to experience orgasm from the pressures alone without intromission. Thus, by synchronizing the movements of her s.o.r. with those of her partner, to give her maximum pressures where they have the most stimulating effect, she can assure herself of more sexual satisfaction.

In addition, her *active* participation in the sex act makes her a true partner—a partner in deed as well as name. This has tremendous psychological value for her, because it is impossible to participate physically in the sexual act without also participating mentally and emotionally. Unfortunately for both males and females, most females, due to faulty teaching or no teaching, are passive participants, if not frigid recipients, in the sex act. Their lack of ecstatic orgasm is due more to lack of participation—mental, emotional, and physical—than any other single causative factor.

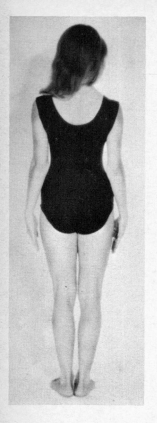
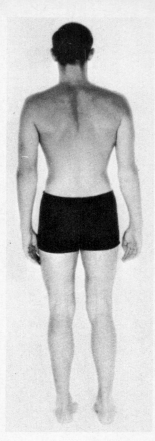

STANDING GLUTEAL SQUEEZE

This is the simplest of gluteal exercises. Stand erect with the heels together. Tighten your posterior and squeeze the buttocks together. At the same time force your s.o.r. forward. Hold this for seven counts and then relax.

If you have difficulty with this, you may try the ballet technique described before, using a silver dollar.

Repeat the exercise five times, take a short rest, and repeat it another five times. This will give you two sets of five repetitions. Be sure to squeeze as hard as you can when you tighten your gluteus maximus muscles, then relax them as much as possible.

Special Instructions: (a) To the wife—when tensing your buttocks, also squeeze your thighs together and make a conscious effort to contract the muscles of your vagina. The alternating contraction and relaxation of these internal muscles will aid you in attaining the highly satisfying vaginal orgasm during intercourse, and will also bring increased pleasurable sensations to your mate. (b) To the husband—when tensing your buttocks and forcing your s.o.r. forward, make a conscious effort to extend and raise your penis. The resulting muscular action will put more "feel" into the sexual act, and heighten the pleasure for both partners.

When the passive wife fails to have an orgasm, or fails to enjoy the sex act, she feels that she is inadequate, that something is wrong with her, that she is indeed a failure sexually. Consequently, she becomes even more passive and sets up a vicious cycle from which there is no easy escape. Her lack of participation, lack of orgasm and pleasure, give her husband a guilt complex. He feels that he is merely using her to satisfy himself. Therefore he has failed her, he is inadequate, he is not a good lover. His ego is hurt in one of its most vulnerable spots, and he becomes less effective as a lover, and may even become impotent.

Developing gluteal control and making use of this during sexual intercourse can make this vital marital act far more exciting, enjoyable, and satisfying for both partners.

The exercises that follow have been specifically devised to give you and your partner this much desired gluteal control.

Some of the exercises in this section are isotonic (with movement) and some are isometric (without movement), and some are a combination of both. Each has been designed to develop control over muscles which are hardly ever used in modern life. For the best possible results follow the instructions carefully.

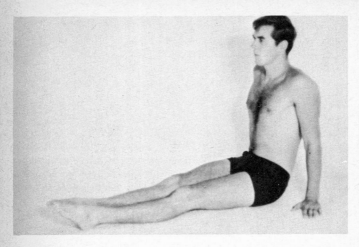

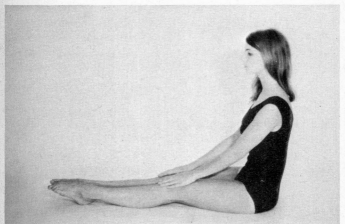

SITTING GLUTEAL SQUEEZE WITH LEGS TOGETHER

Sit on floor with your legs extended and together. Lean back
slightly, and place the palms of your hands on the floor beside
your buttocks. Tighten your gluteus maximus muscles, and squeeze
your posterior cheeks together. Hold this for seven counts, and
then relax as completely as possible. Repeat the exercise five
times, take a short rest, and repeat it another five times.

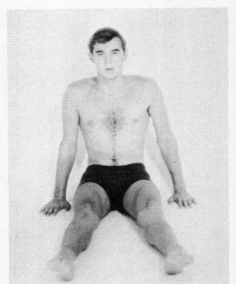

SITTING GLUTEAL SQUEEZE WITH LEGS APART

Sit on the floor with your legs extended and apart. Lean back slightly, and place the palms of your hands on the floor beside your buttocks. Squeeze your buttocks together. Hold for seven counts, and then relax as completely as possible. Do two sets of five repetitions of this exercise.

SIDE-LYING GLUTEAL SQUEEZE

Lie on your left side on the floor. Straighten your body out. Do two sets of five repetitions of the gluteal squeeze. Roll over on your right side and repeat the entire process.

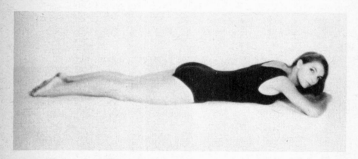

FRONT-LYING GLUTEAL SQUEEZE

Lie face down on the floor. Bend your arms, and rest your head on your bent elbows. Squeeze your gluteus maximus muscles together and press your s.o.r. against the floor. If the pressure is uncomfortable, a pillow may be used. Hold for seven counts, tensing as hard as possible, and then relax as completely as you can. Do two sets of five repetitions of this exercise.

Rapid Variations: This is done exactly as above except that you tense and relax, tense and relax, in rapid succession. Repeat fifteen times at your first practice session. Gradually increase the number of repetitions until you can easily do this one hundred times without stopping for a rest. The entire action should be concentrated in your gluteus maximus muscles.

Note: This exercise may also be done with legs apart.

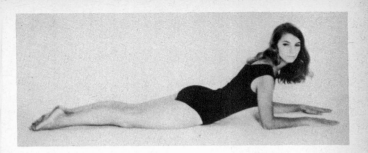

FRONT-LYING GLUTEAL SQUEEZE WITH ELBOW REST

Lie face down on the floor. Bend your arms at the elbows and bring them under your chest so you are resting the weight of your upper body on your forearms and elbows.

(a) Perform two sets of five repetitions of slow method, holding tensed gluteal squeeze for seven counts on each repetition.

(b) Perform one set of fifteen repetitions of the rapid variation, tensing and relaxing in quick succession. Gradually increase the number of repetitions at subsequent practice sessions.

Note: This exercise may also be done with legs apart.

BACK-LYING GLUTEAL SQUEEZE WITH LEGS TOGETHER

Lie flat on your back with your legs extended and held together. Now, repeat all instructions and variations exactly as described for "Back-Lying Gluteal Squeeze with Legs Apart."

Special Instructions: To the wife—when tensing your buttocks also squeeze your thighs together, and make a conscious effort to contract the muscles of your vagina. The alternating contraction and relaxation of these internal muscles will help you to attain the more intense vaginal orgasm and also make the sexual act far more stimulating for your mate.

BACK-LYING GLUTEAL SQUEEZE WITH LEGS APART

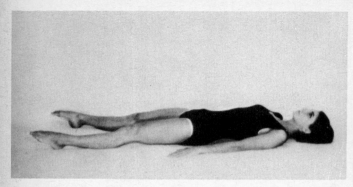

Lie flat on your back with legs extended and apart. Tense your gluteus maximus muscles strongly, and force them together at the same time. Hold this tensed position for seven counts, and then relax as completely as possible. Repeat five times, take a short rest, and repeat five more times. This will give you two sets of five repetitions of this exercise.

Note: With practice it is possible to raise your s.o.r. as much as two inches by merely contracting your gluteus maximus muscles. This is very important to the partner who assumes the underneath position in the common face-to-face method of intercourse because it enables that person to participate vigorously in the act. It is also of value to the person in the above position in this method and to both partners in all methods.

Rapid Variation: This is performed as above except that you tense and relax your buttocks as rapidly as possible again and again. Repeat fifteen times at the first practice session, and gradually increase the number of repetitions until you can do one hundred with ease.

Alternating Variations: Tense the left cheek while leaving the right one relaxed. Then tense the right cheek while leaving the left one relaxed. Do this slowly at first and then faster and faster.

Rotating Variation: This is similar to the "alternating variation" in that one buttock after the other is tensed and relaxed, but this time you strive to get a continuous circular action. Do this both clockwise and counterclockwise.

Comments: All the above variations can be used during the act of intercourse itself to give it more life, make it more stimulating, and bring heightened pleasure to both partners.

BACK-LYING SEAT-RAISE WITH GLUTEAL SQUEEZE

Lie flat on your back with your legs extended and together. Place your arms alongside your body with your palms on the floor. Raise your seat up as high as you can by arching your back, squeezing your buttocks together, and forcing your s.o.r. up as high as possible toward the ceiling. Hold this position for seven counts, and then lower your seat to the floor again and relax completely. Repeat five times, take a short rest, and repeat five more times. This will give you two sets of five repetitions.

Note: This exercise may also be done with legs apart.

DEEP KNEE BEND WITH GLUTEAL SQUEEZE

Stand erect with feet comfortably apart and arms hanging at your sides. Squat down as low as you can go, bending both knees. At the same time raise arms forward to help you maintain your balance. Straighten both knees, and come up to the erect standing position again. As you come up, squeeze your gluteal muscles together, pull your thighs in toward each other, and force your s.o.r. forward. Do two sets of five repetitions of this exercise with a short rest between the two sets.

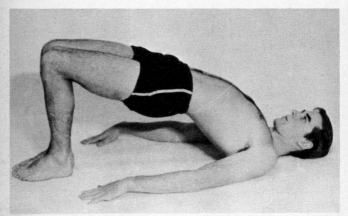

BACK-LYING SEAT-RAISE WITH KNEES BENT

Lie flat on your back with your knees bent at right angles and your feet flat on the floor. Hold your feet and knees together and place your hands flat on the floor beside your buttocks. Raise your seat up as high as you can by arching your back, squeezing your gluteal muscles together, and forcing your sex organ region up as high as you can. Hold this arched position for seven counts, then lower your buttocks to the floor again and relax as much as possible. Do two sets of five repetitions of this exercise with a short rest between the two sets.

Note: This exercise may also be done with feet and knees apart.

FRONT-KNEELING REST WITH LEG EXTENSION

Get down on your hands and knees on the floor. Bring your left knee up to your chest. Then stretch your left leg behind you, and raise it up as high as you can. You should feel a strong arch in your back, especially on the left side. Repeat the exercise five times with your left leg. Then perform the same exercise five times with your right leg. Take a short rest, and do the exercise five more times with each leg.

FRONT-LYING LEG EXTENSION

Lie face down on the floor. Place your hands on the floor beside your face, palms down. Keeping your legs stiff, raise your left leg up as high as possible, arching your back strongly, and then lower your stiff left leg to the floor again. Repeat the same movement with your right leg. Alternate left, then right, until you have raised each leg five times. Take a short rest, and repeat the exercise five more times with each leg.

STANDING STIFF-LEG EXTENSION

Stand erect with your right side to the back of a chair. Place your right hand on the back of the chair for balance. Stiffen your left leg and raise it back as far as it will go. Return leg to starting position beside other leg. Repeat five times, trying to force stiff left leg farther back each time. Turn around, grasp back of chair with your left hand, and perform the same exercise with your stiff right leg, again doing five repetitions. Take a short rest, then do the exercise five more times with each leg.

FRONT-LYING DOUBLE LEG RAISE

Lie face down on the floor, arms alongside your body and palms down. Keeping both legs together and stiff, raise them up as high as you can, squeezing your buttocks together and arching your back as strongly as possible. Pressing down on the floor with palms of your hands will help. Do two sets of five repetitions with a short rest between. This is also a fine lower-back exercise.

Note: This exercise may also be done with legs apart.

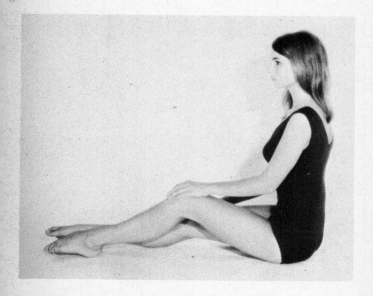

BUTTOCKS-WALK WITH HEELS ON FLOOR

Sit on the floor with your legs extended and together. Place your
hands on your knees. Now, without moving your heels, move your
posterior forward by walking your cheeks forward one after the
other. As you walk forward you must let your knees bend up so
that each buttock can "step" ahead inch by inch. When your
posterior and your heels are almost touching, reverse the direction
and "walk" your buttocks back to the full-length sitting position
again. Walk forward and backward twice.

BUTTOCKS-WALK WITH HEELS ON FLOOR

Sidewalking Variation

Rock up on your right cheek, reach toward your left with your left cheek, taking a *step*, then bring your right buttock in to your left one. Repeat the entire process taking about five or six steps to the left, then reverse the direction and the action and take five or six steps to the right. As you bring your buttocks together after taking a "step" be sure to squeeze them together strongly before taking the next step.

CHAPTER 8

PUT THIGH ACTION
INTO THE SEX ACT

THIGH ROTATION AND THIGH ADDUCTION

Most of the things we had to say about the value of the "gluteal squeeze" also apply to (A) Thigh Rotation and (B) Thigh Adduction. Each of these actions involves the same body parts and helps to develop the kind of control you need for maximum sexual stimulation and satisfaction. Each of them strengthens muscles which are barely used in modern everyday life.

(A) THIGH ROTATION

There are two directions to this action, namely, "inward rotation" and "outward rotation." When performing the inward rotation, the wife should make a conscious effort to squeeze the upper inner parts of her thighs together and

158

try to contract the muscles of her vagina. She should think of gripping the male penis in a milking action. This action, when used in actual sexual intercourse, can add a great deal to her own stimulation and that of her mate. Of course, she must be able to utilize the muscles involved, and that is why these exercises are included.

When performing the outward rotation, the wife should push forward with her s.o.r. In actual sexual intercourse this action will increase the pressures on the entire pubic area for both the man and wife, thereby increasing their pleasure.

When performing the outward rotation, the husband should push forward with his s.o.r. and also try to lift up his penis. In actual intercourse this action will not only increase mutual pressures on the entire pubic area, but will stimulate the wife's clitoris more effectively and increase the "feel" inside the vagina as a whole.

When the actions described above are synchronized during the sex act, so that both man and wife utilize their neuromuscular control to the fullest possible extent, then each will stimulate the other to the maximum degree, and both will achieve the ultimate in sexual enjoyment and satisfaction.

We owe it to ourselves and our mates to do everything within our power to eliminate needless friction and frustration from our lives and to do everything we can to assure both partners a healthy, happy, well-adjusted sex life. The following exercises were designed to contribute materially toward this worthwhile end.

All the exercises described in this section should be done isotonically (with movement) first and isometrically (without movement) afterward. When performing the isometric exercises be sure to go from one extreme to the other holding each for ten counts (approximately six seconds).

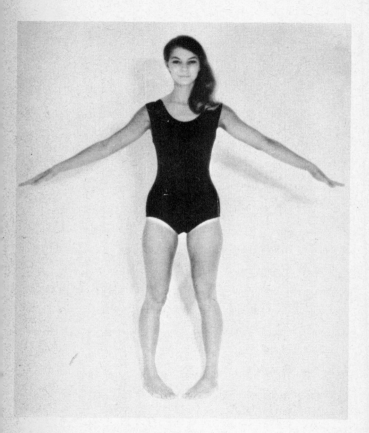

ERECT, STANDING, PIVOT ON HEELS

Stand erect with your feet about ten inches apart. Pivoting on your heels, force your toes inward toward each other as far as they will go. Then force them outward, away from each other, as far as they will go. Continue this thigh-rotating action, going from one extreme to the other each time. Do two sets of four or five repetitions to each set until you can do fifty or more with ease.

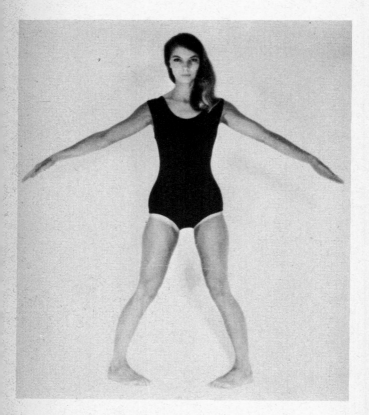

ERECT, STANDING, PIVOT ON TOES

Stand erect with your feet about ten inches apart. Pivoting on your toes, force your heels together toward each other as far as they will go. Then force them outward away from each other as far as they will go. Continue this thigh-rotating action as advised in previous exercise.

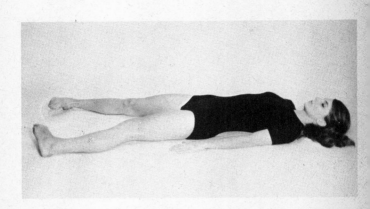

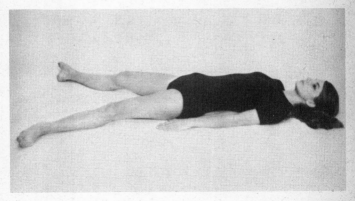

BACK-LYING, PIVOT ON HEELS

Lie back on the floor, legs spread apart and arms alongside body. Pivoting on your heels, force your toes inward toward each other as far as they will go. Then force them outward away from each other as far as they will go. Continue this thigh-rotating action as advised in previous exercise.

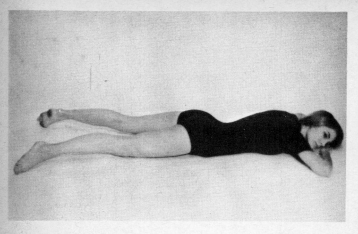

FRONT-LYING, PIVOT ON TOES

Lie face down on floor, arms folded and under head, and legs spread apart. Pivoting on your toes, force your heels together toward each other as far as they will go. Then force them outward away from each other as far as they will go. Continue this thigh-rotating action as advised in previous exercise.

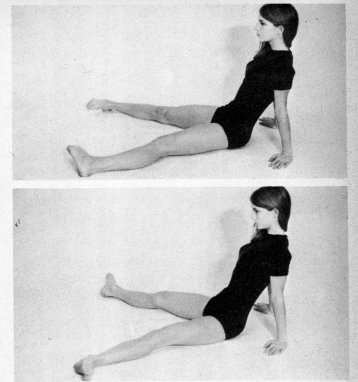

SITTING, PIVOT ON HEELS

Sit on floor with legs straight and spread apart. Pivoting on your heels, force your toes inward toward each other as far as they will go. Then force them outward away from each other as far as they will go. Continue this thigh-rotating action as advised in previous exercise.

Note: The last three exercises can be made more strenuous by wearing a pair of "iron boots." These are attached to the bottom of the feet with straps. The weight of the iron boots provides greater resistance against which your muscles are forced to work. Extra resistance can also be obtained with the help of a training partner. Your partner just grabs your feet and exerts resistance against which you must work. Obviously, the more resistance your partner applies to your feet, the harder you must work in order to rotate your thighs.

(B) THIGH ADDUCTION

There are very few actions in ordinary life which exercise the adductors of the thighs strongly. These muscles pull your legs toward each other. Most of the time your legs move backward and forward, but not very often do they move directly outward or inward. If you happen to use the frog kick when you swim, then your adductors may be in fair condition, as they are used to squeeze your legs together. Wrestlers use their thigh adductors strongly when applying the scissors hold. However apart from these two special cases, the thigh adductors do not get much use.

Our interest in these muscles is twofold. First, we know that variety and intensity can be given to the sex act for both partners when the legs of the bottom partner are wrapped around the body of the top partner—especially during the height of the act, and particularly when great muscular force is exerted. Most of the time the wife assumes the bottom position and is the one who does the leg-wrapping. If her adductors are weak and flabby, and lack tonicity and flexibility, then she will have difficulty using the "body scissors." Furthermore, she will be able to exert very little pressure with her legs around the body of her partner, may experience muscle cramps during the act, or have sore adductor muscles later.

In addition to heightening the body contact for both partners, the body scissors when used by the wife enables her to force her entire sex organ region strongly against that of her husband and also to tilt her pelvis up and down. Therefore it can contribute greatly to clitoric stimulation and thus to more complete sexual satisfaction. Thus, possessing strong, flexible adductor muscles and knowing how to use them can add to the wife's control of the sexual act to her own complete satisfaction, regardless of the skill or lack of skill of her mate. Of course, her strong and vigorous participation will also add greatly to her husband's enjoyment of the sexual act.

The body scissors, when used by the male in the bottom position of the common face-to-face method, gives to the wife the dominant role. The male just hangs on while the female performs most of the action. Such a reversal of roles adds variety, which frequently enables an otherwise "cold" wife to respond. The leg wrap-around can also be used in the side-lying position by either partner, and a partial wrap-around is frequently used in still other positions.

Secondly, the thigh adductors control the inward actions of the thighs as a whole; and the upper, inner parts of the thighs, through which these muscles run, are an integral part of your overall sex organ region. They aid in performing the "pelvic thrust" and "gluteal squeeze" described in detail above, and also play an important part in "thigh rotation." Consequently all of the values attributed to these sections also apply to some extent to the "thigh adduction" described here.

The wife, when performing the exercises that follow, should think of gripping the male penis each time she forces her legs together, not only with her inner thigh muscles (adductors) but also with the walls of her vagina. The husband, when performing the thigh adductor exercises, should push forward and upward with his s.o.r. each time he forces his legs together.

During actual intercourse, the above actions on the part of either partner will add to the enjoyment of the act by both. The most intense pleasures will come only when both partners possess maximum neuromuscular coordination plus the necessary strength, endurance, and flexibility to utilize it to the fullest possible extent. Of course, both partners must also possess sexual know-how and sufficient emotional maturity to be able to utilize it without psychological restraints. The author sincerely believes that the performance of these special exercises can go a long way toward developing the mental, emotional, and physical attributes needed by both partners in the sex act for maximum enjoyment.

PERFORM ISOTONIC (WITH MOVEMENT) EXERCISES FIRST

All the exercises in this section except one (Seated Play-Ball Squeeze) are described with movement (isotonic)

and should be done that way. Only after you have performed the isotonic method should you use the isometric
method.

Some of the exercises described in this section do not
appear to lend themselves readily to isometric (no movement) contraction but do so nevertheless. For example,
in Erect Standing, Wide-Legged Squats, you stand with
your legs spread wide apart and your toes pointed outward. You are told to squat halfway down and then
straighten your legs again. This is isotonic because movement is involved.

To convert this to an isometric exercise you will go
down and *hold* this position for ten counts (approximately
six seconds) while you try with all your might to squeeze
your thighs together. You should feel a strong pull on the
under inner side of your thighs. This is the lower extreme
of the exercise. Now you should straighten your legs to
get to the other extreme of the exercise. Here you squeeze
your stiff legs toward each other as hard as you can without moving your widely spread feet, again counting to ten
so that you *hold* the upper extreme of the exercise for
approximately six seconds. Then go on to the next exercise
and repeat the same process. In each case you must adjust
the isometric contraction to the isotonic exercise which has
been described.

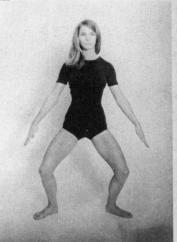

ERECT, STANDING, WIDE-LEGGED SQUATS

Stand erect with feet spread wide apart and toes pointed outward. Squat about halfway down, and then straighten legs again. Do two sets of four or five repetitions at your first training session with a short rest between sets. As your thigh adductors get stronger you should add more repetitions to each of the two sets.

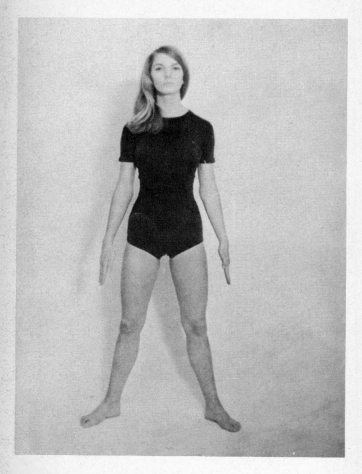

ERECT, STANDING, STRADDLE SLIDE

Stand erect with feet spread apart. Gradually slide feet farther and farther apart until stretch is felt in your crotch. Now, keeping legs straight, force them together again by sliding your feet toward each other with a heel-toe action. Repeat this twice at your first

training session. You can do it more often at subsequent workouts. Do not force yourself beyond a comfortable stretch, and you will gradually develop more strength and flexibility in your thigh adductors without any negative effects.

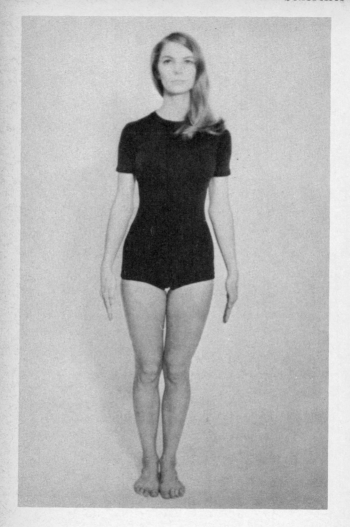

ERECT, STANDING, LONG FORWARD LUNGE

Stand erect with feet together and arms at sides. Take a very long step directly forward with your left foot. Bend forward and place your chest on your left thigh, fingertips touching floor. Bounce body up and down three times, and then return to the erect standing position again. Repeat the entire process with your right foot. Do two sets of four or five long lunges with a short rest between the sets at your first practice session. Gradually add more lunges to each set as your leg muscles get stronger.

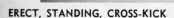

ERECT, STANDING, CROSS-KICK

Stand erect with feet spread about ten inches apart. Raise arms to shoulder level at the sides. Keeping left leg straight, kick it to your right side, crossing it in front of your body. Try to touch your left heel to your right hand. Return left leg to starting position. Repeat same exercise with right leg, this time kicking across your body to your left hand. Alternate, going directly from left to right. Do two sets of four or five alternating cross-kicks with a short rest between sets. Add more repetitions to each set at subsequent practice sessions.

ERECT, STANDING, CROSS-LEGGED BODY TWIST

Stand erect. Cross your right leg behind your left leg, forcing your right foot as far beyond your left foot as possible. Slide your right foot backward away from your left foot so that there is more space between your thighs. Now twist your body hard to the left in a series of hard bouncy movements, trying to twist farther to the left each time. Repeat the same exercises on the other side, reversing all the instructions so that your left leg crosses behind your right. This time you will twist your body hard to the right. Start with one set of four or five twists in one direction, take a short rest, do another set of four or five twists to the other side. At subsequent practices you may add more twists to each repetition.

SEATED KNEE SQUEEZE

Sit on the edge of a chair. Cross your arms on your lap. Place right hand on inner side of the left knee and left hand on inner side of right knee. Lean forward and force your knees as wide apart as they will go——resisting the push of your hands. Now, force your knees together again——this time resisting with your hands. The entire action is done slowly against resistance from the closed position to the wide-open position and then back again. Do two sets of four or five repetitions the first time with a short rest between, and gradually increase the number of repetitions as your adductors and abductors get stronger.

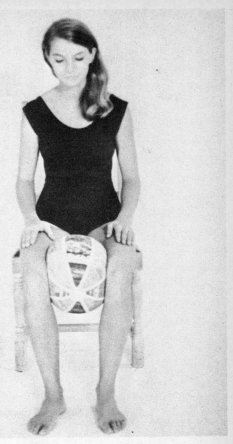

SEATED PLAY-BALL SQUEEZE

Sit on the edge of a chair. Place an inflated rubber ball between
your knees. Squeeze your knees together as hard as you can—
hold for seven counts and then relax. Do this four or five times
in a row, take a short rest, and repeat. Gradually increase number
of repetitions at subsequent practices.

LEG STRETCHING TO SIDES FROM FULL SQUAT

Stand erect with feet apart. Do a full squat, and place both hands on the floor between your knees. Now bounce and stretch your left leg as far as it will go to your left side. Bounce and bring left foot back to starting position again. Bounce again and stretch right leg as far to the right as it will go. Bounce and bring right foot back to starting position again. Repeat, alternating from left to right. Start with two sets of four to five repetitions with a short rest between. Gradually add more repetitions to each set at subsequent practice sessions.

SITTING, LEG STRADDLE

Sit on the floor with your legs together and stretched out in front of you. Spread legs wide apart. Bring legs together again. Continue this action, trying to spread legs wider apart each time. Repeat as advised in previous exercise.

SITTING, LEG STRADDLE, AND CROSS

Sit on the floor with your legs together and stretched out in front of you. Spread legs wide apart. Now, bring them toward each other, cross the left leg under the right, forcing both legs as far as they will go, and then straddle them again. Next time bring the right leg under the left, again forcing legs to cross as much as they can before you straddle them again. Continue this action, alternating the position of the legs as they cross each time. Repeat as instructed in previous exercise.

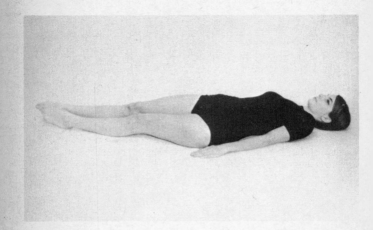

BACK-LYING LEG STRADDLE

This exercise is done exactly the same as "Sitting, Leg Straddle" except that you do it lying flat on your back.

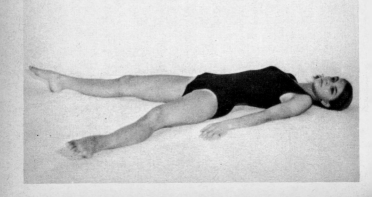

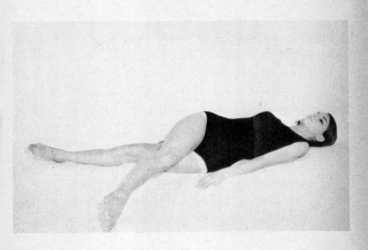

BACK-LYING LEG STRADDLE AND CROSS

This exercise is done exactly the same as "Sitting, Leg Straddle, and Cross," except that you do it lying flat on your back.

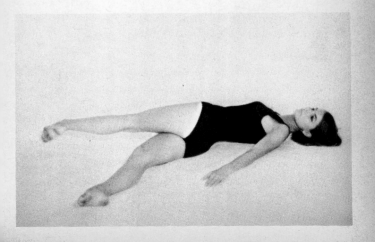

KNEELING REST, SWEEPING LEG CROSS

Get down on your hands and knees. Extend your right leg to your
right side, toes pointed. Sweep your right leg backward toward your
left leg and then beyond your left leg as far as it will go. Then
sweep it back to the starting position again. Pretend there is a
piece of chalk between the toes of your right foot and you are

drawing a big semicircle on the floor behind you. Sweep your right leg from one extreme to the other four or five times in succession. Then repeat the whole exercise with your left leg, again doing four or five continuous sweeps from one extreme to the other. At subsequent practices add more and more repetitions to each of the two sets of cross-sweeps.

SEATED CROTCH STRETCH

Sit on the floor. Bend your knees, and place the soles of your feet
together. Grasp your ankles with your hands, and press down on
your knees with your elbows. Then pull your heels in toward your
crotch as far as they will go. Push feet away, pull feet toward you

again, and so on. Each time you pull your heels toward your crotch try to pull them in a little closer than before, and try to force your knees closer to the floor. Do two sets of four or five repetitions as advised in previous exercise.

BACK-LYING BENT-HIP, BENT-KNEE CROTCH STRETCH

Lie flat on your back on the floor. Bend your legs at the hips and
knees so that your knees are just above your chest. Grasp your legs
from the outside just below your knees, then pull your knees as
wide apart as they will go. While providing resistance with your

hands, slowly force your knees together again. Repeat this action, doing two sets of four to five repetitions with a short rest between sets. Gradually add more repetitions to each set as advised in previous exercise.

FRONT-LEANING REST, JUMPING LEG STRADDLES

Lie face down on the floor. Place hands on floor beside chest and push body up to the common push-up position. Only your hands and feet should be touching the floor, and your body and legs should be straight. Jump your feet wide apart, and jump them together again. Repeat this jumping action, trying to spread your legs wider and wider apart each time. Do two sets of four to five repetitions, and increase the number of repetitions as your body becomes accustomed to this exercise.

BACK-LEANING REST, JUMPING LEG STRADDLE

Sit on the floor. Place hands on floor behind buttocks. Stretch legs
out forward, and raise seat off the floor. Now, keeping seat off
floor, jump legs wide apart and then jump them together again.
Only the hands and the heels should touch the floor throughout
this exercise. Repeat this jumping action, trying to spread your legs
wider and wider apart each time. For your first practice session, do
two sets of four to five repetitions with a short rest between sets.
Gradually add more repetitions to each set as your muscles get
stronger.

SEATED SINGLE LEG STRETCH

Sit on the floor, legs together and extended to the front, and hands on the floor beside your buttocks. Bend your right knee, and grasp your right heel with your right hand. Now, without releasing this heel, stretch your right leg out and bend it again. Repeat this

action four or five times. Then do the same thing with your left hand and left leg. Gradually spread your legs wider and wider apart when doing this exercise, so that you feel more and more stretch in your adductors as well as your hamstrings.

Variation: Perform exercise with both legs at the same time.

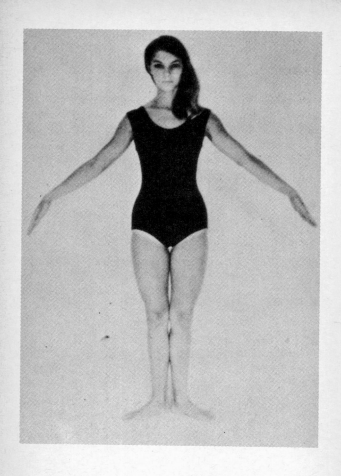

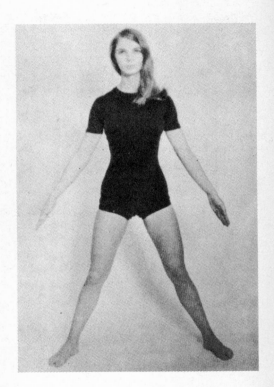

ERECT, STANDING, GRADUALLY SPREADING STRADDLE JUMPS

Stand erect. Jump your feet about a foot apart, then jump them together again, jump them about six inches farther apart and then jump them together again. Continue this straddle jumping, each time spreading your feet wider and wider apart until you reach your limit. Then take a short rest and repeat the whole exercise again. Take about four or five consecutive jumps to reach your widest possible limit. Put a mark on the floor for each of your feet and then try to go a little farther at each succeeding practice.

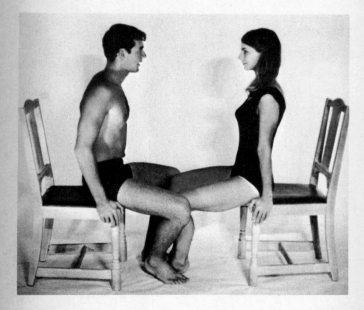

A

SEATED PARTNER THIGH SQUEEZE AND SPREAD

Place two chairs two feet apart and facing each other. Partners sit on the chairs facing each other with their knees touching. (A) The male partner places his knees outside the knees of his female partner. He then squeezes his knees together while the female tries to spread her knees apart. (B) The female partner places her

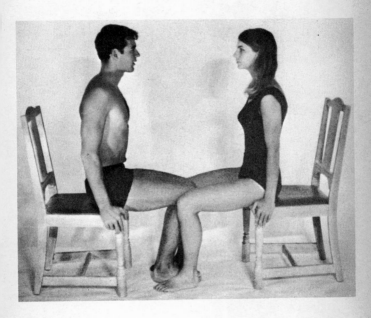

B

knees outside the knees of the male. She then squeezes her knees
together while the male partner tries to spread his knees apart.

This is a very severe exercise and brings into play muscles which
are seldom used in everyday life. Therefore both partners are advised to proceed slowly at first.

CHAPTER 9

A FLABBY MID-REGION CAN RUIN YOUR SEX LIFE

TRUNK FLECTION AND EXTENSION

Few muscle groups in modern man and woman are as flabby as those of the mid-region, not only those of the abdomen but those of the lower back. Flabby abdominal muscles are the first sign of soft living. Here, too, overeating soon shows itself in excess layers of unwanted, unhealthy blubber. Bulging bellies add nothing to the sex appeal of either partner, nor to the performance of the sex act. Neither do weak abdominal muscles, because intercourse does require some movement at the mid-region.

Almost invariably, lower back pain accompanies weak abdominal muscles. To compensate for the excess weight at the front, one must bend slightly backward, thus subjecting the lower back muscles to constant tension. To make matters worse, most of the physical acts we perform in our everyday life we do to the front of us and below shoulder level. This encourages us to bend forward, round the spine, tip the pelvis forward, and again place extra strain on the lower back muscles. Of course, the weaker these muscles are, the more back pains we will suffer.

200

Finally, most women and an ever-increasing number of men, wear some kind of foundation garment to hold themselves in and provide the support that the muscles used to give. These merely aggravate the negative condition that already exists and hasten muscular deterioration. Thus flabby muscles get even flabbier and make their plight known through more and more aches and pains.

Whenever the trunk is raised, or the legs are raised, or the body is bent at the waist, the abdominal muscles are involved. Whenever the back is arched, the muscles of the lower back are brought into play. Whenever the hips are turned on the trunk, or the trunk is twisted on the hips, various mid-region muscles must be contracted. Whenever the pelvis is tilted up or down, muscles of this region come into play. It is impossible to participate in the sexual act without involving all your major mid-region muscle groups, and the more vigorous the participation, the more strongly are these muscles involved.

Only regular systematic exercise can strengthen the muscles of your mid-region, or, for that matter, any other muscles in your body. Only exercise can give your muscles tonicity, flexibility, and staying power. Since some exercises are better than others, we have selected here the best for the revitalizing of your important mid-region muscles. Performing these exercises will not only make you look better and feel better but will also eliminate many needless muscular aches and pains. More important still, from the standpoint of this book, they will make you a much more efficient sex partner.

GENERAL INSTRUCTIONS

Unless otherwise indicated, each of the exercises that follow should be done in two sets of four or five repetitions with a short rest between sets. At succeeding practice sessions more repetitions can be added to each set to force your muscles gradually to work harder and harder. (See isometric instructions at end of this chapter.)

(A) TRUNK FLECTION EXERCISES

All the exercises in this group bring into play the trunk flexors and especially your abdominal muscles, and involve bending at the waist. In some cases the legs are static and the trunk moves, in others the trunk is static and the legs move, but the muscular work is similar in both cases.

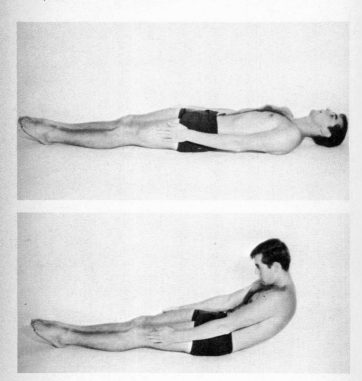

BACK-LYING CURL-UP

Lie flat on your back, legs together and hands on your thighs. Raise your head, lower your chin to your chest, and slowly curl your body up. At the same time slide your hands down your thighs toward your knees. Come up as high as you can, and then lower your back to the floor again by uncurling slowly. Repeat as advised.

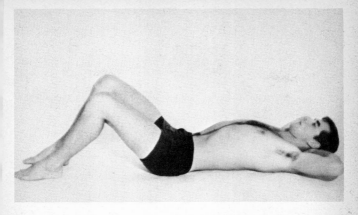

BACK-LYING TWISTING SIT-UPS

Lie flat on your back, clasp your hands behind your head, and hook your feet under something to hold them down. Sit up and twist hard to your left, trying to touch your right elbow to your left knee. Lie back again. Sit up again and twist hard to your right, trying to touch your left elbow to your right knee. Lie back again. Repeat, alternating from side to side.

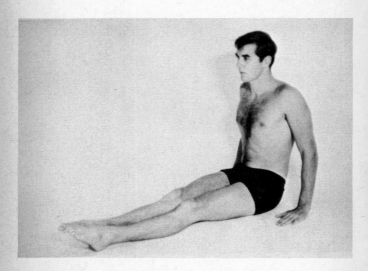

SITTING, PULL KNEES TO CHEST

Sit on the floor with your legs together and stretched out in front of you. Place hands on floor beside buttocks. Slide both feet toward buttocks, and knees toward chest. As knees approach chest, clasp both arms around shins and pull knees in hard to the chest. Lower hands to starting position and stretch legs out in front again. Repeat.

Variation: This exercise may be done one leg at a time. It is easier this way and may be used to lead up to using both legs for those who have very weak abdominal muscles.

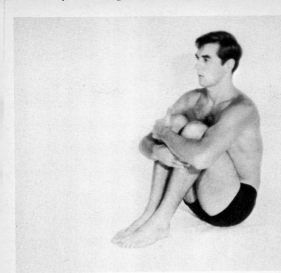

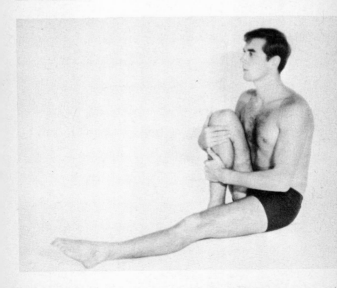

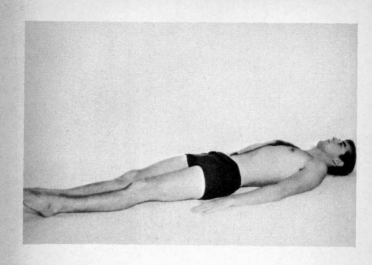

BACK-LYING, PULL KNEES TO CHEST

Lie flat on your back, legs together, arms alongside body. Double up both knees, wrap arms around knees as they approach chest, and pull knees in hard to the chest. Lower hands to floor again as you stretch legs upward and forward and lower them as slowly as possible to the floor again. Repeat.

Variation: This exercise may be done with one leg at a time for those with weak abdominal muscles as it is easier this way. When the abdominal muscles are strong enough, both legs may be used at the same time.

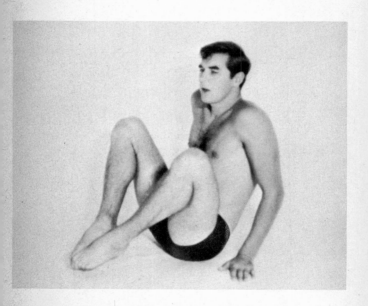

V-SIT, PULL KNEES TO CHEST, AND STRETCH LEGS

Sit on floor, with legs together and stretched out in front and
hands on the floor behind the buttocks. Lean trunk back until it
forms an angle of about 45 degrees with the floor. Bend your knees,
slide your heels toward your buttocks, then raise your feet off the
floor and bring your knees in to your chest. Next, extend both
legs upward and forward so that they form a V with your trunk.
Hold this V as long as you can, and then lower your stiff legs to the
floor as slowly as possible. Continue until strain is felt, and then
stop for a short rest before doing your second set.

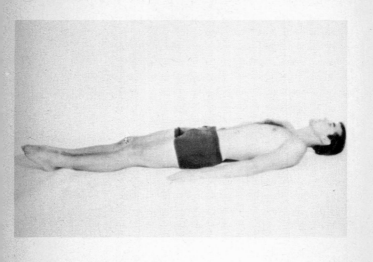

BACK-LYING LEG RAISES

Lie flat on your back, legs together and stretched out, hands on floor close to your sides. Keeping legs stiff, raise them up off the floor and bring them up until your toes are just above your face. Lower stiff legs to floor again. Repeat.

Variation: Instead of stopping upward movement of legs when toes are above face, continue action of legs until toes touch the floor beyond the head. Body must roll back for this, and the legs should be spread wide apart.

STANDING ALTERNATE KNEE PULLS

Stand erect, feet together, arms hanging at sides. Bend left knee
and bring it up toward your chest. Wrap arms around left shin as

knee comes up, and pull knee in to chest. Lower left foot to the
floor again. Repeat same procedure with your right knee. Continue
exercise, alternating from left to right.

STANDING ALTERNATE HIGH KICKS

Stand erect, feet together, arms held out at shoulder level on the sides. Kick your left leg up as high in front as you can. Lower left foot to floor and kick right leg up as high in front as you can. Continue exercise, alternating from left to right. Keep leg as straight as possible while kicking.

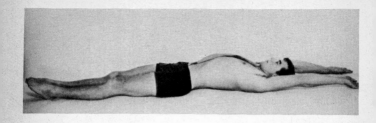

BACK-LYING V RAISE AND LOWER

Lie flat on your back with your arms extended beyond your head, your legs together and stretched out. Now, bend quickly at the waist, raising both your trunk and your legs off the floor at the same time. Hands should touch toes at the height of the trunk-and-leg raise. It requires considerable mid-region strength as well as balance to perform this correctly. As soon as hands touch toes, drop back and legs to the floor again and repeat.

BACK-LYING FLUTTER KICK OF LEGS

Lie flat on your back with your legs together and straight. Press hands firmly on floor beside buttocks. Raise stiff legs about seven inches off the floor, hold them there, and flutter your legs up and down as if swimming the crawl stroke. Continue as long as you can, and then drop your legs to the floor again. This is a difficult exercise requiring considerable mid-region muscular strength. At first you may have difficulty even getting your heels off the floor, but with practice you will find it easier and easier.

(B) TRUNK EXTENSION EXERCISES

All the exercises in this group bring into play the muscles of your lower back, and involve straightening up from the bent-over position or arching the back. Although in some cases the legs are fixed and the trunk moves, and in others the trunk is fixed and the legs move, the muscular work is similar.

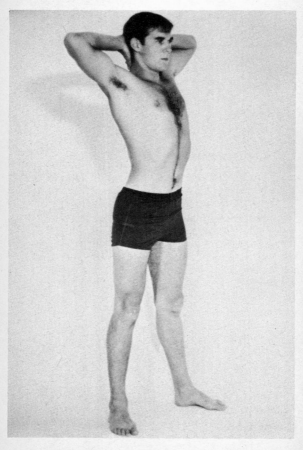

ERECT, STANDING, TRUNK BENDING

Stand erect with legs spread apart and hands clasped behind head. Bend forward at the waist as far as possible, and then raise trunk and bend slightly backward. Repeat. Keep the knees straight, and try to bend farther forward each time you do this exercise.

ERECT, STANDING, TRUNK CIRCLING

Stand erect with the feet apart and hands on hips. Bend forward at the waist, circle to the left, then bend backward, circle to the right, bend forward, and circle to the left again. Continue this

trunk-circling action (counterclockwise). Repeat the same exercise going in the opposite (clockwise) direction. Do one set of four or five repetitions in one direction, take a short rest, and do another set of four or five repetitions in the other direction.

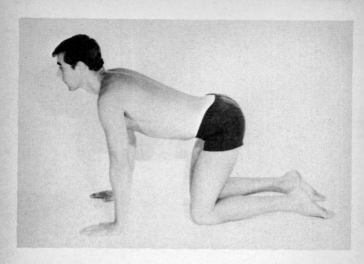

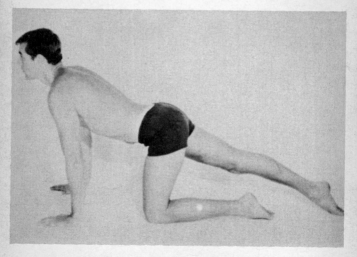

KNEELING-REST LEG RAISE

Get down on your hands and knees. Extend your right leg behind you, pointing the toes. Raise right leg up as high as it will go and lower to floor again, always keeping it straight. Repeat. Perform the same exercise with your left leg extended behind you.

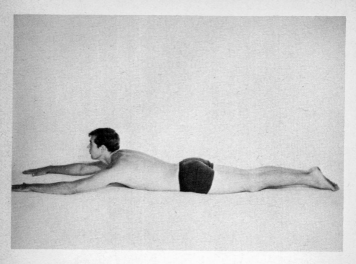

FRONT-LYING LEG RAISE

Lie face down on the floor with your legs together and stretched out and your arms extended beyond your head. Raise your right leg up as high as it will go and then lower it to the floor again. Do the same with your left leg. Repeat, alternating from right to left.

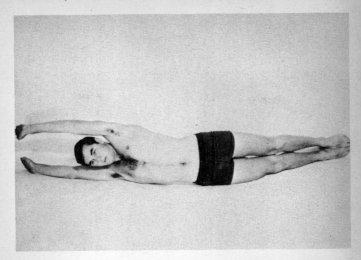

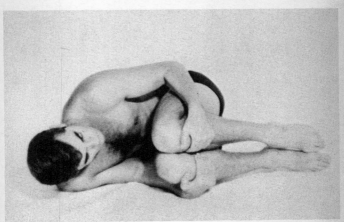

SIDE-LYING DOUBLE UP AND ARCH

Lie on your left side on the floor. Double up in a ball, wrapping your arms around your shins. Straighten your body out and arch your back strongly. Arms must be extended beyond the head. Double up again. Repeat. Do the entire exercise on your right side exactly as already described.

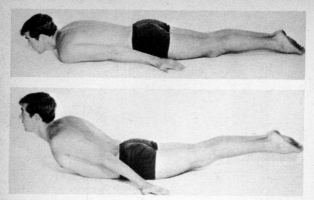

FRONT-LYING TRUNK RAISE

Lie face down on the floor. Raise your head and shoulders up as high as they will go by arching your back, and lower trunk to floor again. Repeat.

Note: This exercise can be made more severe by clasping hands behind neck, and still more strenuous by extending the arms beyond the head. It can be made easier by hooking your heels under something solid.

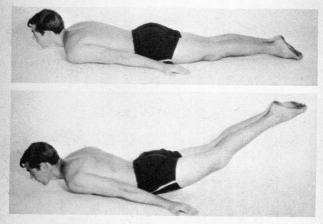

FRONT-LYING DOUBLE LEG RAISE

Lie face down on the floor with your arms alongside your body and your hands flat on the floor. Arch your back strongly, and raise both legs up as high as they can go. Lower legs to floor again. Repeat.

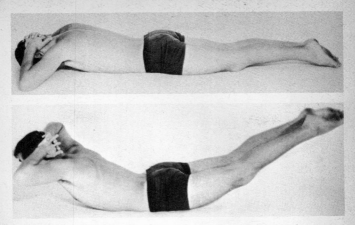

FRONT-LYING ARCH

Lie face down on the floor with your legs straight and together and your hands clasped behind your head. Arch your back strongly and raise your legs and your head and shoulders up as high as they will go. Repeat.

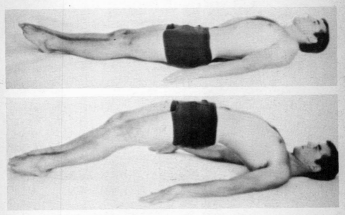

BACK-LYING ARCH

Lie back on the floor, legs straight and together, arms alongside body with the palms on the floor. Press down on your arms, and arch your back as strongly as possible by forcing your stomach up in the air. Lower back to floor again. Repeat, trying to arch higher up each time.

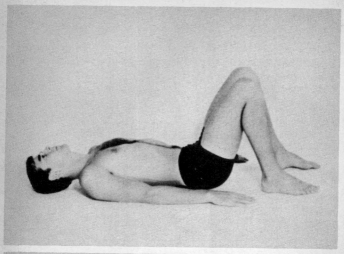

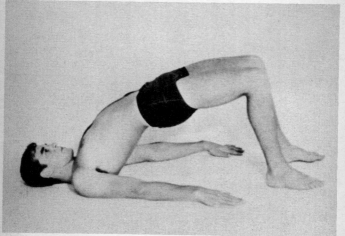

BACK-LYING, BENT-KNEE ARCH

Lie back on the floor, knees bent, feet flat on the floor, arms alongside body with the palms facing down. Pressing down on your arms and your feet, raise your stomach up as high as possible, arching your back strongly. Lower buttocks to floor again. Repeat, trying to arch up higher each time.

FRONT-LEANING REST ON CHAIR WITH LEG KICK

Stand erect about a foot from a chair. Bend forward and place your hands on the chair. Straighten out your body. Now, keeping your right leg stiff, kick it backward and upward and high as it will go. Do the same thing with your left leg. Repeat, alternating from one leg to the other. Try to kick leg a little higher back each time.

ISOMETRIC INSTRUCTIONS

You may have wondered how you are going to convert some of the isotonic (movement) exercises in this section into isometric (no movement) exercises. For example, in "Back-Lying Curl-Up," you start lying flat on your back (this is one extreme of the exercise) and then sit up as far as possible (this is the other extreme). It seems impossible to contract your abdominal muscles against *resistance* at the two extremes of this exercise when there is none.

In all exercises of this type you must provide the necessary resistance at both extremes of the exercise. The simplest way of doing this is with the help of a training partner. It is up to this partner to provide the resistance at both extremes of the exercise.

To make this absolutely clear let us return to "Back-Lying Curl-Up." At the beginning of the exercise, while you are still lying on your back, your partner places one hand on your chest and holds you down. You then try with all your might to sit up against this resistance, while you count to ten (approximately six seconds). This adequately takes care of one extreme of the exercise.

If you do the curl-up correctly you will probably reach a "sticking point" about three quarters of the way up to a sitting position (the other extreme of the exercise). If this is the case, then you just *hold* this sticking point on the upward trip for ten counts (approximately six seconds), and the conversion from isotonic to isometric for that exercise will be satisfactorily completed.

If you are able to come up to the sitting position easily, then your partner will have to provide a sticking point by placing a hand on your chest just before you reach the top, or upper extreme, of the upward action. In this case you will try with all your might to complete the last few inches of the exercise against this immovable resistance while you count to ten (approximately six seconds).

Resistance may also be provided by a rope, a bar, a piece of furniture, or some similar object, or by the use of exercising weights. However, the principle is always the same—if your own body does not provide the resistance you need at both extremes of the isotonic exercise, in order to convert it into an isometric exercise, then you must make use of outside resistance as described above.

CHAPTER 10

SPECIAL SEXOMETRIC
EXERCISES

SPECIAL SEXOMETRIC EXERCISES

Although detailed instructions have been given throughout this book to enable you to convert any isotonic (movement) exercise into an isometric (no-movement) exercise, a number of special sexometric exercises are included in this chapter for a very definite purpose.

Frankly, most people are lazy when it comes to physical exertion. Many will start off on this highly specialized exercise program like a house on fire, but no matter how great the benefits may be, very few will continue this program indefinitely.

Fortunately, once you have gone through the entire program outlined in this book and have rehabilitated all the muscles so important to the sex act, it is possible to *maintain* good muscle tone with very little additional exercise.

Earlier in this book you were advised to train a minimum of 15 minutes per training session three times every week. During the first two weeks you may feel stiff as a result of the new demands made upon your muscles. By the third week your muscles should be well adjusted. At the end of six weeks there should be very noticeable results. Though continued improvement will result from continued training sessions there will be less and less progress as you get closer and closer to your absolute limits in strength, flexibility, endurance, and neuromuscular coordination.

By the end of three months of conscientious training there will be very little additional improvement, but, if you stop exercising completely, your muscles will soon lose everything they have gained. However, you can maintain your gains through an isometric exercise program which involves only about 2½ minutes of muscular contraction once every two weeks.

This is possible because an isometric contraction need only be held for ten counts (approximately six seconds) for maximum benefits.

The exercises described in this section have been designed to reach every muscle group involved in any of the isotonic exercises described in this book. Therefore, by following this special sexometric exercise program you will be able to maintain the results which you have obtained through your three months of concentrated effort. Best of all, you need perform each exercise only once every two weeks, and each exercise need only take six seconds to perform.

It is important that you do not skip any of these biweekly training sessions. If you do, some deterioration will immediately set in. It is much easier to maintain than to re-develop good muscle tone.

The following exercises have been especially selected to serve the purposes already described above. These should be sufficient to meet the purposes of this book. However, if additional isometric exercises are desired, they should be selected from the exercises outlined in previous chapters, and they should be performed in the same manner as those described below. In all cases, each exercise is performed only once during any one training session, and the contraction is held for only ten counts (approximately six seconds).

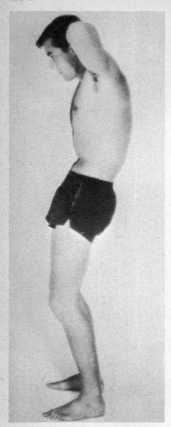

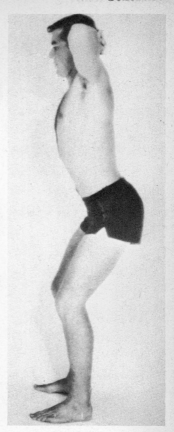

ERECT, STANDING, FORWARD-UPWARD PELVIC THRUST

Stand erect with the feet slightly apart and the hands on the thighs. Pull in your stomach and thrust your s.o.r. (sex organ region) forward and upward as high as it can go. Hold this position for the count of ten (approximately six seconds) and then relax.

ERECT, STANDING, BACKWARD-DOWNWARD PELVIC THRUST

Stand erect with the feet slightly apart and the hands on the hips. Lift your buttocks up as you hollow your back and thrust your s.o.r. downward and backward as far as it will go. Hold this position for the count of ten and then relax.

**HALF-SQUAT,
FORWARD-UPWARD
PELVIC THRUST**

Stand erect with feet apart. Squat about halfway down, hands behind neck. Thrust your s.o.r. forward and upward as high as it will go and hold for six seconds.

**HALF-SQUAT,
BACKWARD-DOWNWARD
PELVIC THRUST**

Stand erect with feet apart. Squat about halfway down, hands behind neck. Thrust your s.o.r. downward and backward as far as it will go and hold for six seconds.

SITTING, FORWARD-UPWARD PELVIC THRUST

Sit on floor, legs straight and slightly apart, hands on floor behind
buttocks. Thrust your s.o.r upward and forward as high as it will
go and hold for ten counts.

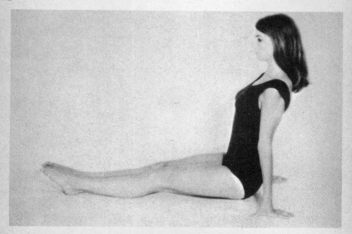

SITTING, BACKWARD-DOWNWARD PELVIC THRUST

Sit on floor, legs straight and slightly apart, hands on floor behind
buttocks. Thrust your s.o.r. downward and backward as far as it will
go and hold for ten counts (approximately six seconds).

BACK-LYING WITH KNEES BENT, FORWARD-UPWARD PELVIC THRUST

Lie back on the floor with knees bent and feet slightly apart. Thrust your s.o.r. upward and forward as high as it will go and hold as advised.

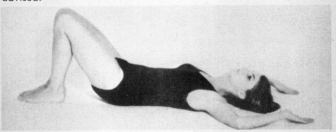

BACK-LYING WITH KNEES BENT, BACKWARD-DOWNWARD PELVIC THRUST

Lie back on the floor with knees bent and feet slightly apart. Thrust your s.o.r. downward and backward as far as it will go and hold as advised.

FRONT-LYING, RESTING WEIGHT ON FOREARMS, FORWARD-UPWARD PELVIC THRUST

Lie face down on the floor with legs straight and slightly apart. Bend your elbows, and place your forearms and the palms of your hands on the floor beneath your chest. Raise upper body so that chest does not touch floor. Thrust your s.o.r. forward and upward as high as it will go and hold.

FRONT-LYING, RESTING WEIGHT ON FOREARMS, BACKWARD-DOWNWARD PELVIC THRUST

Lie face down on floor as instructed immediately above. With weight of upper body resting on the forearms, thrust your s.o.r. downward and backward as far as it will go and hold.

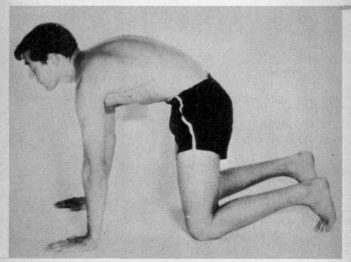

FRONT-KNEELING REST, FORWARD-UPWARD PELVIC THRUST

Get down on your hands and knees on the floor. Spread knees slightly. Thrust your s.o.r. forward and upward as high as it will go and hold as advised.

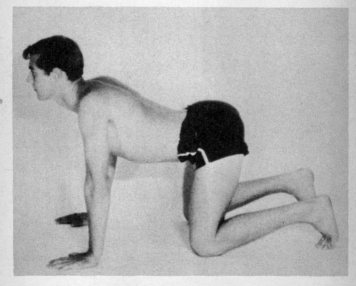

FRONT-KNEELING REST, BACKWARD-DOWNWARD PELVIC THRUST

Get down on your hands and knees on the floor. Spread knees slightly. Thrust your s.o.r. downward and backward as far as it will go and hold.

ERECT, STANDING, THRUST HIPS TO LEFT AND THEN TO RIGHT

Stand erect with the feet spread apart. Thrust hips strongly to your left and hold for six seconds. Relax. Thrust hips strongly to your right and hold for six seconds.

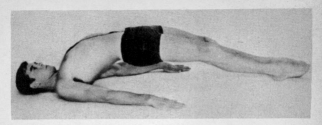

BACK-LYING WITH LEGS STRAIGHT, UPWARD PELVIC THRUST

Lie flat on your back with your legs straight and spread slightly apart, arms alongside your body, palms on the floor. Arch your body as strongly as you can, thrusting your s.o.r. up as high as possible and hold for ten counts.

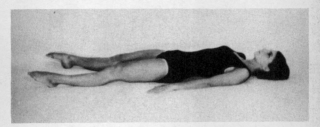

BACK-LYING GLUTEAL SQUEEZE

Lie flat on your back with your legs straight and slightly apart. Squeeze your gluteus muscles (buttocks) tightly together and hold for ten counts.

FRONT-LYING GLUTEAL SQUEEZE, RESTING ON FOREARMS

Lie face down on the floor. Bend elbows and place forearms on floor beneath your chest. Raise upper body so that chest does not touch floor. Squeeze your gluteus muscles (buttocks) tightly together and hold for ten counts.

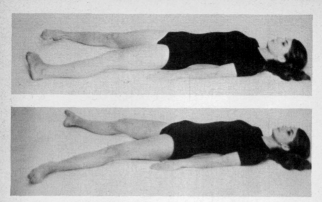

BACK-LYING THIGH ROTATION

Lie flat on your back, legs spread apart and arms alongside your body. Rotate your thighs inward, by forcing your toes toward each other as far as they will go and hold for six seconds. Relax. Rotate your thighs outward by forcing your toes away from each other as far as they will go and hold for six seconds.

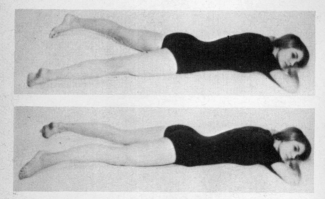

FRONT-LYING THIGH ROTATION

Lie face down on the floor, arms folded under the head and legs spread apart. Pivoting on your toes, rotate your thighs inward by forcing your heels away from each other as far as they will go and hold for six seconds. Relax. Rotate your thighs outward by forcing your heels toward each other as far as they will go and hold for six seconds (ten counts).

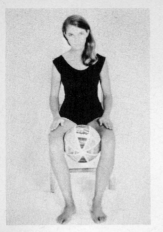

SEATED THIGH ADDUCTION

Sit on the edge of a chair. Place a ball between your knees, and squeeze your legs together as hard as you can while you count to ten (approximately six seconds).

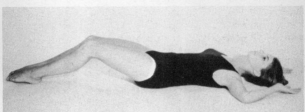

BACK-LYING THIGH ADDUCTION

Lie back down on the floor, knees slightly bent and together, arms beside head. Squeeze your legs together as hard as you can while you count to ten.

FRONT-LYING THIGH ADDUCTION

Lie face down on the floor, arms in front of body and legs together. Squeeze your legs together as hard as you can and count to ten.

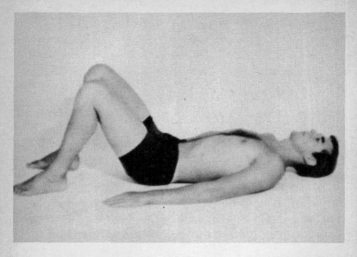

STATIC ABDOMINAL CONTRACTION

Lie flat on your back with your knees bent and your feet flat on
the floor. Tense your abdominal muscles as hard as you can and
hold for ten counts (six seconds). Relax. Stretch your legs out and
roll over on your left side. Tense your abdominal muscles as hard
as you can and hold for ten counts. Relax.

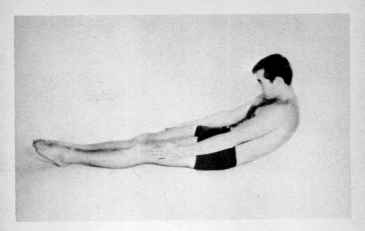

BACK-LYING CURL-UP

Lie flat on your back, hands on your thighs. Raise your head and shoulders off the floor, and slide your hands up your knees. Hold this position for ten counts.

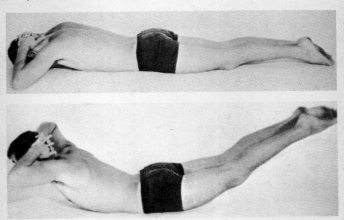

FRONT-LYING BACK ARCH

Lie face down on the floor, legs straight and together, with your hands clasped behind your head. Raise your chest and legs off the floor by arching your back as strongly as possible. Hold this position for six seconds (ten counts).

PSYCHOSOMATIC VAGINAL CONTRACTION
(for the wife only)

Lie flat on your back. Concentrate on your vagina, and try as hard as you can to contract the muscular walls of your vagina. Hold this vaginal contraction for ten counts and then relax.

PSYCHOSOMATIC CONTRACTION OF THE PENIS
(for the husband only)

Sit on the floor with your knees bent and your feet flat on the floor. Place your hands on the floor behind your buttocks. Concentrate on your penis, and try as hard as you can to contract the muscles which raise it. Hold this contraction for six seconds (ten counts) and then relax.